Sculpture Collection
of the
Cincinnati Art Museum

Sculpture Collection

of the
Cincinnati Art Museum

92860

Title page illustration: 1939.233, Bust of Tyche
Crowned with the Zodiac, Nabataean, early I c. A.D.

To John J. Emery
Trustee, President, Chairman
Patron and Benefactor

Contents

1906.40, Warrior, Etruscan, VI-Vc. B.C.

1946.7, Donor of the Hospice of Salins, French, XIII c.

Introduction

When the Museum opened its doors in the spring of 1886 the art of sculpture was represented by the marble carvings of Cincinnati's own Hiram Powers and several of his neo-classic contemporaries as well as by a plentiful supply of plaster casts. This was the aesthetic logic of the times, and the casts were taken, at several removes, from such commonly agreed-on masterpieces as the Laocoon, Venus of Milo, the Victory of Samothrace, the pediments and frieze of the Parthenon.

In the following decades the cast collection was systematically developed to incorporate early and later Gothic examples, the Renaissance in France and Italy. Egypt was represented by one cast and Assyria by two. There was also an inclusive group of so-called "fictile ivories," casts from the Symmachorum panel on through the Renaissance. A climax was reached in the 1890s with the acquisition of an entire issue of the Elkington Company's base-metal reproductions of gold, silver and bronze masterpieces from all periods, not excepting the Sasanian and Celtic Christian. And remarkably accurate and deceptive reproductions they were. The doric Schmidlapp Wing of 1907 was designed primarily to house the cast collection.

They are all retired from exhibition now except for occasional decorative use, but along with their conscientious and no doubt educational assemblage came another systematic collecting of plaster originals by contemporary sculptors, largely American. These were the first fixed impressions of the modeller's clay, ready for carving or bronze-casting. The line of demarcation between the original and reproduction is hard to draw in these instances, and it was probably the changing of artistic fashion as much as changing aesthetic philosophy that kept most of them from surviving on exhibition. A notable exception is the tomb effigy of Elizabeth Boott Duveneck by her famous husband, assisted by Clement Barnhorn, as well as Barnhorn's own "Alma Mater" from which the stone trumeau of the Covington, Kentucky, cathedral was carved.

Another such problem is posed by Houdon's plaster portrait bust of Jean-Jacques Rousseau, acquired much later. These often-repeated plaster versions made under the sculptor's supervision could be closer to his original intention than were the inevitably shrunken terra cottas and marbles carved at second hand by skilled assistants.

Through all this a kind of Gresham's Law seemed to operate; not that reproductions drove out originals, when there were so few to drive out, but rather that reproductions kept originals from coming in. And at base the difference between a reproduction and an original is the difference between death and life. By this modern logic the Museum is convinced that a III century B.C. Greek marble copy of Myron's V century bronze heifer is incomparably preferable to a plaster cast of a Roman copy of the Discobolos.

In 1939, a turning point came with the acquisition and installation of the Nabataean sculptures excavated by Dr. Nelson Glueck on the mountaintop site of Khirbet Tannur in Trans-Jordan, as it was then called. Unique except for a parallel and currently unexhibited group in the possession of the Jordanian Government their controlled but intense life-force edged many well-worn, re-painted Graeco-Roman casts into the wings.

By 1946 all casts and other reproductions except for the few borderline cases already cited, disappeared from public view, and the present collection began to take form. It was an auspicious moment to begin; prices had not yet risen altogether beyond the Museum's grasp, and several major masterpieces from Egypt, Greece, China and medieval France were still available on the American market. A temporary eddy in the current of collecting taste made it possible to lay the foundations of the Near Eastern section, both ancient and Islamic, now, possibly because of that temporary neglect, the most exceptional phase of the collection.

The arrangement and classification of the sculptures for the purposes of this catalog are of necessity arbitrary. Patriarchal bronze vessels from the Shang and Chou Dynasties of China for instance, as well as the "mild silver and furious gold" of Persia should perhaps be grouped as toreutic objects, their correct if somewhat ponderous identification. But something in the sheer authority of their presence, most imprecise words, demands their consideration as works of sculpture. So too with certain ceramic objects; are they subjects for taxonomy or simply sculpture in a different material? The object itself decides.

In the early years, shortly before and after the Museum's founding, there was a feeling abroad that anything rare or curious or informative should be deposited in it. Hence the Museum's ethnological collections are extensive, consisting of many thousands of artifacts not many of which rise to the level of art. The boundary between artifact and work of art cannot be precisely surveyed, but a fairly strict line has been drawn here to divide from the anthropological majority a handful of American Indian and African sculptures that might so qualify as well as a small group of later American objects vaguely termed "folk art." At least they have been on continuous recent exhibition.

This catalog is primarily pictorial. The temptation to write an outline history of the arts in terms of sculpture has been resisted, even though the range of the collection might conceivably justify it. Essential vital statistics are, however, included: *Place of Origin* where known or reasonably conjectured; *Material*; *Date* by reasonable conjecture; *Dimensions* including weight where precious materials are concerned;

Accessions Number, a matter of reasonable pride on the part of the present administration; *Author* when known; *Collection History* when known, with dealers' names cited only when the object has been identified by dealers' ownership in public exhibition catalogs or other publications; *Exhibition History* as far as known; *Publication History* as complete as possible. Some textual comment is occasionally added, to record pertinent oral communications or to indicate significant comparisons.

A living collection, and its catalog, is a work always in progress. Additional data continually come to light. But it is assumed that the reader equipped with the basic information given here can pursue his studies of individual sculptures as far as his needs or interest may dictate.

Many people have collaborated in the compiling of this catalog. Under the general editorship of the Director preliminary work was done by Pinkney Near, Curator of Painting from 1963-1965; Dr. Carol Macht, Curator of Decorative Arts and Miss Priscilla Perry. Miss Carolyn R. Shine, Registrar, has done inestimable basic work since the beginning, and assisted by Mrs. Renate Farmer, Associate Curator of Education, has accomplished the final collation.

Noel Martin has been deeply involved throughout, not only as the typographer but as an organic designer of the whole undertaking. For the photographs illustrating this catalog the Museum is indebted to F. V. Raymond, who has been associated with the Museum since 1900, and to Dutro Blocksom, C. W. Bostain, the late Richard Mathers, Frank Caro, the Curt Valentin Gallery and Jerry Morgenroth.

Above all the Ford Foundation must be thanked for the matching grant which initiated the project.

Philip Rhys Adams, *Director*

Catalog and Illustrations

Egypt

1962.701

1962.700

1962.700
PALETTE IN SHAPE OF A FISH, pre-Dynastic, 4000-3000 B.C. Slate, height 2¹⁷⁄₃₂ (6.4), width 5³⁄₃₂ (12.9), depth ³⁄₁₆ (0.5).
Published: *Cincinnati Art Museum Bulletin*, VII, 3-4, Feb. 1965, illustrated.

1962.701
PALETTE, pre-Dynastic, 4000-3000 B.C. Slate, height 11³¹⁄₃₂ (30.4), width 4¾ (12.0), depth ¹¹⁄₃₂ (0.9).
Published: *Cincinnati Art Museum Bulletin*, VII, 3-4, Feb. 1965, illustrated.

1945.62

STANDING FIGURE OF ROYAL SCRIBE,
XII Dynasty, 2000-1788 B.C. Black granite, height 18
(45.7), width 6²⁹⁄₃₂ (17.5), depth 8⁹⁄₁₆ (21.7).
Inscribed: (translated by Henri Capart) back of
block, "Cenn-Beff-Ny, Chancellor of the documents
of the king, born from a royal concubine."
Published: *Cincinnati Art Museum Guide*, 1956, p. 6;
Ancient Civilizations, Cincinnati, 1961, No. 5.

1947.343
HEAD OF A SCRIBE, XII Dynasty, 2000-1788, B.C.
Gray granite, height 4⅛ (10.5), width 4¹³⁄₃₂ (11.2),
depth 3⁷⁄₁₆ (8.7).
Gift of Millard F. and Edna F. Shelt.

1947.60
HEAD OF A SCRIBE, XII Dynasty, 2000-1788 B.C.,
said to have been found at Heliopolis. Dark granite,
height 4¹⁵⁄₁₆ (12.6), width 5¹⁵⁄₁₆ (15.0), depth 3³¹⁄₃₂ (10.1).
Gift of Millard F. and Edna F. Shelt.

1947.1
DOUBLE CROCODILE FIGURES, XII Dynasty,
2000-1788 B.C., said to have been found in the Fayum.
Granite (in high relief), height ⁹⁄₁₆ (1.4), width 1⅝
(4.2), depth 2¹⁵⁄₃₂ (6.3).
Gift of Millard F. and Edna F. Shelt.

1945.63
FRAGMENT OF A HEAD OF QUEEN
HATSHEPSUT (as a man), XVIII Dynasty, from
temple at Deir-el-Bahri, 1493-1479 B.C. Rose granite,
height 10½ (26.6) width 7⅝ (19.4), depth 4⅞ (10.7).
Oral communications from Herbert E. Winlock and
Ambrose Lansing confirmed the provenance, from
the Metropolitan Museum's 1927-1928 excavations at
Deir-el-Bahri.
Published: *Cincinnati Art Museum Guide*, 1956, p. 7;
Ancient Civilizations, Cincinnati, 1961, No. 6;
Emma Swan Hall, "Some Ancient Egyptian Sculpture
in British Collections," *Apollo*, March 1968, p. 168,
caption fig. 13; Hall, "Some Ancient Egyptian Sculp-
ture in American Museums," *Apollo*, July 1968, p. 14,
fig. 16, note 27, p. 17.
Exhibited: *A Concert of Masterpieces*, Columbus
Gallery of Fine Arts, Oct. 1939, No. 3.

1945.62

1945.63

1966.266

1966.266

PORTRAIT OF A NOBLEWOMAN, from
Asiyut, XVIII Dynasty, ca. 1385-1375 B.C. Limestone
with traces of polychromy, height 19½ (49.5), width
13⅝ (34.6), depth 10%₆ (26.8).
Inscribed: (translated by Klaus Baer) on back, three
vertical columns, beginning at the right,

"A boon which the King gives to Hathor, Lady of
Medjed, Lady of Heaven, Mistress of the Gods ...
... Wepwawet gives to me ...
... Hathor, Lady of Medjed. It is the songstress of
Amon Re"

Beginning at the left for the three columns written in
the opposite direction,

"... the gods
... a good life, praying for old age for him, adoring ...
... to all the Gods of Upper Egypt, endowments."

Published: *The Art Quarterly,* XXIX, 3-4, 1966, p. 289,
illus., p. 292; *Gazette des Beaux-Arts,* Feb. 1967, p.
54, No. 207; *Cincinnati Art Museum Bulletin,* VIII,
2-3, Jan. 1968, p. 22.
Given by his friends in memory of Joseph D.
Nelson, Jr.

1961.287

HEAD OF A YOUNG NOBLEMAN, XVIII
Dynasty, 1580-1350 B.C. Limestone with polychromy,
height 5%₆ (13.8), width 5½ (14.0), depth 4%₆ (11.3).
Published: "La chronique des arts," *Gazette des
Beaux-Arts,* No. 1129, Paris, Feb. 1963, p. 18, fig. 79;
Motour (Cincinnati Automobile Club), Feb. 1964,
illustrated p. 7; *Cincinnati Art Museum Bulletin,* VII,
3-4, Feb. 1965, illustrated; B. L. Zimmerman,
"Adventures in Art," *The Wonderful World of Ohio,*
32, 1, Jan. 1968, pp. 8-11, illustrated.
Gift of Mr. and Mrs. John J. Emery.

1961.287

1927.333

1927.333
DOOR JAMB RELIEF (fragment from tomb of
Panhesy), Tel-el-Amarna, XVIII Dynasty, 1369-1358
B.C. Stone, height 11⅛ (28.2), width 15½ (38.3).
Inscribed: (translated by George R. Hughes) on left,
". . . behold(s) Aton every day, the heart . . ."
Published: J. D. S. Pendlebury, *The City of
Akhenaton, Part III: The Central City and the
Official Quarters. The Excavations at Tel-el-Amarna
During the Seasons 1926-27 and 1931-36*, Memoir 44
of the Egypt Exploration Society, Vol. I: Text 1951,
p. 27, No. S.91; *Ancient Civilizations*, Cincinnati,
1961, No. 7.
Gift of the Egypt Exploration Society.

1924.397 and .398
TWO FRAGMENTS OF INCISED RELIEF
FROM THE ROYAL MANGERS SHOWING
THE LEGS OF CATTLE, Tel-el-Amarna, XVIII
Dynasty, 1369-1358 B.C. Limestone, (1924.397) height
10⁷⁄₁₆ (26.5), width 19¹⁵⁄₁₆ (50.6); (1924.398) height 10¼
(26.0), width 10¹³⁄₁₆ (27.5).
Published: F. G. Newton, *Illustrated London News*,
July 12, 1924.
Gift of the Egypt Exploration Society.

1927.332 joined to 1927.334
TWO FRAGMENTS FROM A ROYAL
FIGURE, Tel-el-Amarna, XVIII Dynasty, 1369-1358
B.C. Hard white limestone, height 6½ (16.6), width
6¹⁵⁄₁₆ (17.6), depth 3⅝ (9.2).
Gift of the Egypt Exploration Society.

1927.335
FRAGMENT FROM A ROYAL FIGURE,
Tel-el-Amarna, XVIII Dynasty, 1369-1358 B.C. Hard
white limestone, height 3⁷⁄₁₆ (8.8), width 2⅝ (6.7),
depth 2½ (6.4).
Gift of the Egypt Exploration Society.

1919.500
HEAD OF A SCRIBE, XVIII Dynasty, 1580-1350
B.C. Black granite, height 4½ (11.4), width 4¾ (12.0),
depth 3¾ (9.5).
Gift of the heirs of John W. Bookwalter

1919.500

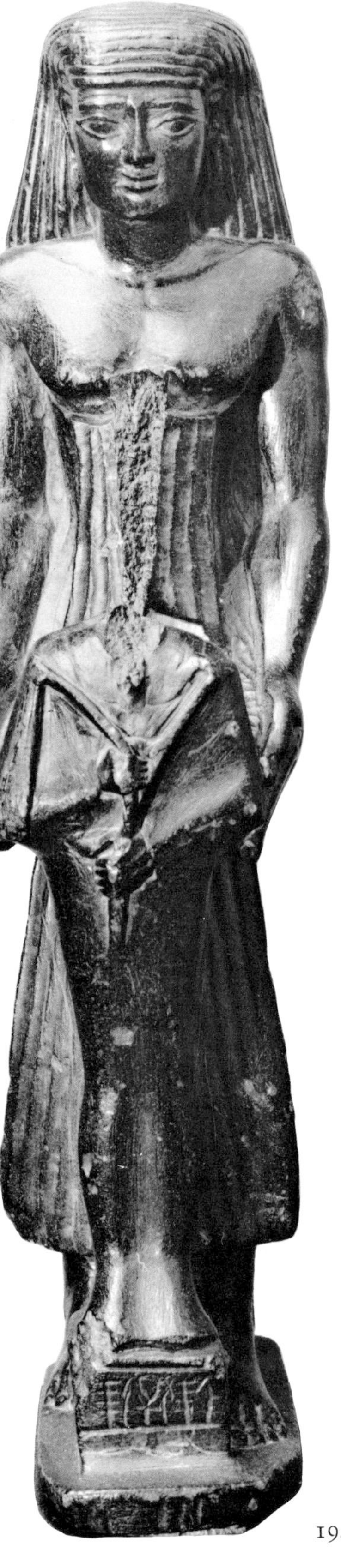

1947.390

1947.23
KNEELING FIGURE HOLDING OSIRIS BEFORE HIM, XVIII Dynasty, 1580-1350 B.C.
Brown granite, height $7\frac{7}{8}$ (20.0), width 3 (7.6), depth $4\frac{11}{32}$ (11.0).
The kneeling figure possibly represents the Prime Minister of Amenhotep III.
Gift of Millard F. and Edna F. Shelt.

1947.390
PRIEST OF AMON WITH OSIRIS, said to have been found at Karnak, Legrain excavations, XVIII Dynasty, 1580-1350 B.C. Black basalt,
height $9\frac{7}{8}$ (25.15), width $2\frac{19}{32}$ (6.5), depth $3\frac{3}{8}$ (8.6).
Inscribed: on back and side, "Say a prayer to Osiris, Amon of Thebes, for an offering to Wapu, Lady of Reverence."
Published: "Cincinnati Art Museum News," *Magazine of Art,* Nov. 1947, p. iii, illustrated.
Collections: Kelekian; Jules Bache, New York.
Gift of Millard F. and Edna F. Shelt.

1947.55
STELA, SEPULCHRAL RELIEF, XVIII Dynasty, 1580-1350 B.C. Painted limestone, height $10\frac{27}{32}$ (27.5), width $8\frac{5}{16}$ (21.1), depth $1\frac{3}{4}$ (4.5).
Gift of Millard F. and Edna F. Shelt.

1926.69
HEAD (probably of Rameses II 1292-1225 B.C.), Abydos. Limestone, height $6\frac{7}{32}$ (15.8), width $3\frac{1}{2}$ (8.9), depth $2\frac{1}{16}$ (5.2).
Gift of the Egypt Exploration Society.

1915.458
MUMMY MASK, Ballabysh, XIX Dynasty, 1350-1205 B.C. Wood, height $13\frac{1}{16}$ (33.2), width $7\frac{3}{4}$ (19.7), depth $3\frac{9}{16}$ (9.0).
Gift of the Egypt Exploration Society.

1947.25
HEAD OF NEFRETIRI, XIX Dynasty, 1292-1225 B.C. Buff stone relief, height $3\frac{3}{16}$ (8.1), width $3\frac{9}{32}$ (8.3), depth $\frac{21}{32}$ (1.7).
Gift of Millard F. and Edna F. Shelt.

1945.64

1945.64
SETI I OFFERING TRUTH TO THOTH,
Abydos, 1313-1292 B.C. Limestone with traces of
polychromy, height 30¼ (76.9), width 42⁷⁄₁₆ (107.8).
Published: *Cincinnati Art Museum Guide*, 1956, p. 5;
Ancient Civilizations, Cincinnati, 1961, No. 8; James
B. Pritchart, *The Ancient Near East in Pictures
Relating to the Old Testament*, Princeton University
Press, 1954, No. 522, p. 191 and 318.

1945.64

1945.65

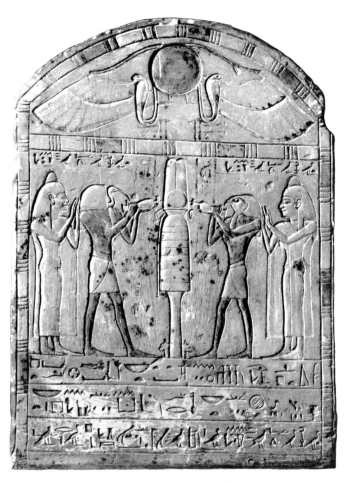

1947.392

1945.65
SEKHMET, XIX Dynasty, 1350-1205 B.C. Black
granite, height 28⅜ (72.3), width 20 (51.4), depth
17⅝ (44.7).
The socket on top of the head indicates an original
head-dress, probably a Hathor symbol of the moon
disk flanked by cow's horns.
Published: *Ancient Civilizations*, Cincinnati, 1961,
No. 1.

1947.17
STANDING FIGURE OF NEFER-TUM
XXII Dynasty, 954-745 B.C. Bronze, height 6¹⁵⁄₁₆ (17.6),
width 1⁹⁄₁₆ (4.0), depth 3⅛ (7.9).
Inscribed: on base, as yet undeciphered.
Gift of Millard F. and Edna F. Shelt.

1947.392
STELA: SEPULCHRAL TABLET OF
TA-KHAA-EN-BAST, Abydos, XXII Dynasty,
945-745 B.C. Incised limestone with polychromy,
height 13 (33.0), width 9⅜ (24.0), depth 2½ (6.4).
Inscribed: (translation) "An offering which the king
gives (to) Osiris, Foremost of the Westerners, Lord of
Abydos, (that) he may grant funerary offerings of
bread and beer, cattle, and fowls, and all things
good and pure for the Ka of the Lady Ta-Khaa-en-
Bast, daughter of the Scribe of the Divine Rolls of
Anhur, Pabarema."
Collections: Lady Meux.
Gift of Millard F. and Edna F. Shelt.

1947.398

1947.400

1947.397

1947.399

Set of Four Canopic Jars, said to have been found at Sakkara, XXVI Dynasty, 663-525 B.C. Limestone. Each has a double row of hieroglyphics down the front (translation by William F. Albright).

1947.397
JAR WITH COVER IN THE FORM OF A MAN'S HEAD, container for the mummified liver and dedicated to Amesty, lord of the South. The inscription invoked the goddess Isis. Height 12³⁄₁₆ (30.9), diameter 6⁵⁄₈ (16.8).

1947.398
JACKAL-HEADED JAR, container for the mummified stomach and dedicated to Dewamutef who presided over the East. The inscription was dedicated to the goddess Neit. Height 11¹³⁄₁₆ (30.0), diameter 6¹⁄₁₆ (15.4).

1947.399
BABOON-HEADED JAR, container for the mummified lungs and heart and dedicated to the baboon-headed god Hepy. The inscription invoked the protection of the goddess Nephthys. Height 12 (30.4), diameter 6⁵⁄₁₆ (16.0).

1947.400
HAWK-HEADED JAR, container for the mummified intestines and dedicated to Qebeh-Senewef, lord of the West. The sixth-century scribe made a mistake in the inscription: he invoked the goddess Sokaris instead of Selket which would have been more correct in earlier usage. Height 12³⁄₈ (31.3), diameter 6⁵⁄₁₆ (16.0).
Published: *Ancient Civilizations*, Cincinnati, 1961, No. 10.
Gift of Millard F. and Edna F. Shelt.

1947.98
STANDING FIGURE OF ANUBIS, said to have
been found at Sakkara, XXVI Dynasty, 663-525 B.C.
Bronze, height 4½ (11.4), width 2⅛ (5.3), depth
1¼ (3.2).
Inscribed decoration and hieroglyphics on front
of base.
Gift of Millard F. and Edna F. Shelt.

1947.67
STANDING FIGURE OF BAST, said to have
been found at Memphis, XXVI Dynasty, 663-525 B.C.
Bronze, height 3¹⁵⁄₁₆ (10.0), width 1½ (3.8),
depth 1½₂ (2.6).
Gift of Millard F. and Edna F. Shelt.

1947.15
SEATED FIGURE OF A CAT, XXVI Dynasty,
663-525 B.C. Bronze, height 6⅜ (16.3), width 2⁷⁄₁₆
(6.2), depth 4⅜ (11.1).
Gift of Millard F. and Edna F. Shelt.

1926.23
HEAD OF A CAT, XXVI Dynasty, 663-525
B.C. Bronze, height 4⁹⁄₁₆ (11.6), width 3⁹⁄₁₆ (9.1),
depth 4¼ (10.8).
Exhibited: *Carnival of Animals,* Columbus Gallery
of Fine Arts, Dec. 2-31, 1950.
Collections: Mrs. A. Floyd Delafield, ca 1875-1880.
Gift of Mary Eva Keys.

1947.402
HAWK WEARING THE DOUBLE
CROWN, said to have been found at Memphis,
XXVI Dynasty, 663-525 B.C. Bronze, height 7⁹⁄₁₆ (19.2),
width 2⁹⁄₃₂ (5.8), depth 5³⁄₁₆ (13.15).
Gift of Millard F. and Edna F. Shelt.

1947.96
SEATED FIGURE OF IMHOTEP, said to have
been found at Memphis, XXVI Dynasty, 663-525 B.C.
Bronze, height 4⁷⁄₃₂ (10.7), width 1⅜ (3.5), depth
1⁷⁄₁₆ (3.6).
Gift of Millard F. and Edna F. Shelt.

1947.96

25

1947.97
SEATED FIGURE OF ISIS WITH HORUS
IN HER LAP, said to have been found at Zagazig,
XXVI Dynasty, 663-525 B.C. Bronze, height 5 (12.7),
width 1⁵⁄₁₆ (3.3), depth 1⁵⁄₁₆ (3.3).
Gift of Millard F. and Edna F. Shelt.

1947.383
BUST OF ISIS, XXVI Dynasty, 663-525 B.C. Green
stone, height 3⁵⁄₁₆ (8.4), width 2³⁄₁₆ (5.5), depth 1¹¹⁄₁₆ (4.3).
Gift of Millard F. and Edna F. Shelt.

1947.401
STANDING FIGURE OF OSIRIS, said to have
been found at Memphis, XXVI Dynasty, 663-525 B.C.
Bronze, height 12²⁹⁄₃₂ (32.3), width 3¹⁄₁₆ (7.7), depth
2⁵⁄₃₂ (5.5).
Gift of Millard F. and Edna F. Shelt.

1947.299
STANDING FIGURE OF OSIRIS, XXVI
Dynasty, 663-525 B.C. Bronze, height 5⅝ (14.1), width
1⅜ (3.5), depth ¹³⁄₁₆ (2.1).
Gift of Millard F. and Edna F. Shelt.

1947.391
STANDING FIGURE OF OSIRIS, XXVI
Dynasty, 663-525 B.C. Bronze, height 13⁷⁄₁₆ (34.2),
width 3⅝ (9.2), depth 2⁹⁄₁₆ (6.4).
Gift of Millard F. and Edna F. Shelt.

1947.56
SEATED FIGURE OF OSIRIS, said to have
been found at Memphis, XXVI Dynasty, 663-525 B.C.
Black granite, height 10¹⁷⁄₃₂ (26.8), width 2¹⁵⁄₁₆ (7.5),
depth 4¹⁵⁄₁₆ (12.5).
Gift of Millard F. and Edna F. Shelt.

1947.298
STANDING FIGURE OF OSIRIS, XXVI
Dynasty, 663-525 B.C. Bronze, height 6½ (16.5), width
1¾ (4.4), depth 2⁹⁄₃₂ (2.3).
Gift of Millard F. and Edna F. Shelt.

1947.62
STANDING FIGURE OF PTAH, XXVI
Dynasty, 663-525 B.C. Bronze, height 4⅛ (10.5), width
1⁹⁄₁₆ (4.0), depth 2⁵⁄₃₂ (2.0).
Gift of Millard F. and Edna F. Shelt.

1947.391

1947.297
SEATED FIGURE OF SEKHMET, found at
Bubastis, XXVI Dynasty, 663-525 B.C. Bronze, inlaid
gold eyes, height 11⅝ (29.7), width 2⁵⁄₁₆ (5.85),
depth 4¹⁵⁄₃₂ (11.35).
Inscribed: along side of base.
Published: "Cincinnati Art Museum News,"
Magazine of Art, Nov. 1947, p. iv, illustrated.
Gift of Millard F. and Edna F. Shelt.

1947.100
STANDING FIGURE OF AMON-RE, said to
have been found at Desuk, XXVI Dynasty, 663-525
B.C., or later. Bronze, height 5¹³⁄₁₆ (14.7), width 1¹⁄₁₆
(2.65), depth 1¹⁵⁄₁₆ (5.0).
Gift of Millard F. and Edna F. Shelt.

1947.61
AMON-RE, XXVI Dynasty, 663-525 B.C, or later.
Bronze, height 5¾ (14.6), width 1¹⁄₁₆ (2.7), depth
1¹⁷⁄₃₂ (3.9).
Gift of Millard F. and Edna F. Shelt.

1947.337
ANUBIS ON PAPYRUS COLUMN, XXVI
Dynasty, 663-525 B.C., or later. Bronze, height 6¾
(17.2), width 1⁷⁄₃₂ (3.1), depth 2⅞ (7.3).
Gift of Millard F. and Edna F. Shelt.

1947.14
STANDING FIGURE OF BAST, said to have
been found at Bubastis, XXVI Dynasty,
663-525 B.C., or later. Bronze, height 4¹⁵⁄₁₆ (12.5), width
1½ (3.8), depth 1⁹⁄₃₂ (2.9).
Gift of Millard F. and Edna F. Shelt.

1947.28
STANDING FIGURE OF BAST, said to have
been found at Tell Basta, XXVI Dynasty, 663-525
B.C., or later. Bronze, height 3¾ (9.5), width ²⁷⁄₃₂ (2.1),
depth 1⅝ (4.15).
Gift of Millard F. and Edna F. Shelt.

1947.103
STANDING FIGURE OF BAST, said to have
been found at Desuk, XXVI Dynasty, 663-525 B.C.,
or later. Bronze, height 3¾ (9.5), width 1³⁄₁₆ (3.0),
depth ²³⁄₃₂ (1.8).
Gift of Millard F. and Edna F. Shelt.

1947.297

1947.382
HEAD OF A CAT, said to have been found at Bubastis, XXVI Dynasty, 663-525 B.C., or later. Bronze with gold earring, height $4\frac{3}{4}$ (12.1), width $3\frac{1}{8}$ (7.9), depth $3\frac{9}{16}$ (9.0).
Gift of Millard F. and Edna F. Shelt.

1947.18
SEATED FIGURE OF A CAT, XXVI Dynasty, 663-525 B.C. or later. Bronze, height $3\frac{11}{16}$ (9.4), width $\frac{7}{8}$ (2.2), depth $1\frac{5}{8}$ (4.1).
Gift of Millard F. and Edna F. Shelt.

1947.364
FISH, said to have been found at Edfu, XXVI Dynasty, 663-525 B.C., or later. Bronze, height $1\frac{7}{8}$ (4.8), width $\frac{27}{32}$ (2.2), depth $4\frac{7}{16}$ (11.3).
Gift of Millard F. and Edna F. Shelt.

1947.104
SEATED NUDE FIGURE OF HARPOKRATES (the child Horus), said to have been found at Memphis, XXVI Dynasty, 663-525 B.C., or later. Bronze, height $4\frac{15}{16}$ (12.5), width $1\frac{11}{32}$ (4.6), depth $\frac{7}{8}$ (2.2).
Gift of Millard F. and Edna F. Shelt.

1947.19
STANDING NUDE FIGURE OF HATHOR, XXVI Dynasty, 663-525 B.C., or later. Bronze, height $6\frac{21}{32}$ (16.9), width $1\frac{3}{4}$ (4.5), depth $\frac{7}{8}$ (2.3).
Gift of Millard F. and Edna F. Shelt.

1947.64
HAWK ON RECTANGULAR CASE, XXVI Dynasty, 663-525 B.C., or later. Bronze, height $3\frac{3}{4}$ (9.5), width $1\frac{21}{32}$ (4.2), depth $4\frac{11}{16}$ (11.9).
Gift of Millard F. and Edna F. Shelt.

1947.370
IBIS, XXVI Dynasty, 663-525 B.C., or later. Bronze, height $3\frac{29}{32}$ (9.9), width $2\frac{1}{4}$ (5.7), depth 6 (15.2).
Published: "Cincinnati Art Museum News," *Magazine of Art*, Nov. 1947, p. iv.
Gift of Millard F. and Edna F. Shelt.

1947.16
STANDING FIGURE OF KHNUM, XXVI Dynasty, 663-525 B.C., or later. Bronze, height $7\frac{5}{32}$ (18.2), width $1\frac{15}{16}$ (4.9), depth $2\frac{3}{32}$ (5.3).
Gift of Millard F. and Edna F. Shelt.

1947.371
SEATED FIGURE OF KHONSU, XXVI Dynasty, 663-525 B.C. or later. Bronze, height $12\frac{7}{16}$ (31.6), width $2\frac{1}{2}$ (6.4), depth $2\frac{1}{32}$ (5.1).
Gift of Millard F. and Edna F. Shelt.

1947.4
SEATED FIGURE OF MAAT, said to have been found at Memphis, XXVI Dynasty, 663-525 B.C., or later. Bronze, height $2\frac{1}{4}$ (5.5), width $\frac{7}{8}$ (2.2), depth $\frac{3}{4}$ (1.9).
Gift of Millard F. and Edna F. Shelt.

1947.3
STANDING FIGURE OF MIN, XXVI Dynasty, 663-525 B.C., or later. Bronze, height $2\frac{31}{32}$ (7.5), width 1 (2.54), depth $\frac{9}{16}$ (1.4).
Gift of Millard F. and Edna F. Shelt.

1947.336
STANDING FIGURE OF MUNT, or Horus, XXVI Dynasty, 663-525 B.C., or later. Bronze, height $7\frac{15}{16}$ (20.2), width $2\frac{11}{16}$ (6.8), depth $2\frac{11}{16}$ (6.8).
Gift of Millard F. and Edna F. Shelt.

1947.22
STANDING FIGURE OF MUT, XXVI Dynasty, 663-525 B.C., or later. Bronze, height $5\frac{5}{8}$ (14.2), width $1\frac{1}{4}$ (3.2), depth $1\frac{1}{8}$ (2.8).
Gift of Millard F. and Edna F. Shelt.

1947.57
STANDING FIGURE OF NEIT, XXVI Dynasty, 663-525 B.C., or later. Bronze, height $10\frac{29}{32}$ (27.7), width $2\frac{1}{4}$ (5.7), depth $3\frac{11}{16}$ (9.4).
Inscribed: on base.
Gift of Millard F. and Edna F. Shelt.

1947.57

1957.145

1957.149

1947.73
OSIRIS with ded on back, crown of Upper
Egypt with plumes of Aton, XXVI Dynasty, 663-525
B.C., or later. Bronze, height 4²⁹⁄₃₂ (12.5), width 1¼
(3.2), depth 1⅞ (2.2).
Gift of Millard F. and Edna F. Shelt.

1947.59
STANDING FIGURE OF SEKHMET AND
OBELISK, XXVI Dynasty, 663-525 B.C., or later.
Bronze, height (incl. prongs) 8⅜ (21.3), width
1³¹⁄₃₂ (5.0), depth 2¹⁵⁄₁₆ (7.5).
Gift of Millard F. and Edna F. Shelt.

1947.27
TAUERET, said to have been found at Damanhous,
XXVI Dynasty, 663-525 B.C., or later. Bronze, height
3⁹⁄₁₆ (9.0), width ¹¹⁄₁₆ (1.7), depth 1 (2.5).
Gift of Millard F. and Edna F. Shelt.

1957.145
KNEELING HORUS, XXVI-XXX Dynasties,
663-322 B.C. Bronze, height 10¹¹⁄₁₆ (27.1), width 5¹⁵⁄₁₆
(15.0), depth 3⅞₁₆ (11.2).
The uniform scoring of the surface suggests that a
thin layer of gold was originally pressed over the
figure, possibly before the technique of mercury
gilding mentioned by Vitruvius was generally used.
Published: *Ancient Civilizations*, Cincinnati,
1961, No. 2.
Gift of Mr. and Mrs. James H. Stone.

1957.149
SEATED FIGURE OF SEKHMET, XXVI-XXX
Dynasties, 663-322 B.C. Bronze, height 25⁷⁄₁₆ (64.6),
width 5¼ (13.3), depth 11¹³⁄₁₆ (30.0).
Sekhmet is here represented with a male instead
of the usual female body.

1947.99
STANDING HARPOKRATES (the child Horus),
XXVI-XXX Dynasties. Bronze, height 5⁵⁄₁₆ (13.6),
width 1½ (2.6), depth 1²⁹⁄₃₂ (4.8).
Gift of Millard F. and Edna F. Shelt.

1947.101
SEATED OSIRIS, XXVI-XXX Dynasties. Bronze,
height 4⁵⁄₁₆ (10.9), width 1⅜ (3.5), depth 1¹⁵⁄₃₂ (3.7).
Gift of Millard F. and Edna F. Shelt.

1953.123

1952.8

1947.24
CROUCHING IBIS, XXVI-XXX Dynasties. Bronze, height $4\frac{1}{8}$ (10.5), width $1\frac{7}{8}$ (4.7), depth $3\frac{15}{16}$ (10.1).
Gift of Millard F. and Edna F. Shelt.

1947.365
STANDING FIGURE OF ANHUR, found at Mittrahaine, Persian Dynasty, 525-332 B.C. Bronze, height $4\frac{11}{16}$ (11.9), width $1\frac{21}{32}$ (3.5), depth $1\frac{5}{8}$ (4.1).
Gift of Millard F. and Edna F. Shelt.

1947.26
SPHINX, said to have been found at Mittrahaine, near Cairo, 525-332 B.C. Bronze, height $2\frac{7}{16}$ (6.3), width $1\frac{13}{32}$ (3.6), depth $4\frac{3}{8}$ (11.0).
Gift of Millard F. and Edna F. Shelt.

1952.8
PTOLEMY PHILADELPHOS OFFERS A LIBATION (fragment of incised relief), Sebennytos (Sammanud), 285-247 B.C. Granite, height $52\frac{1}{4}$ (132.3), width $33\frac{1}{4}$ (84.5).
Inscribed: (translated by George Steindorff), before Ptolemy, "offering a libation to his father"; before Osiris, "I bestow upon you the kingdom of Horus and his throne"; below, "the golden Horus, he whom his father has crowned, the King of Upper and Lower Egypt, the Lord of the two Lands."
Published: George Steindorff, "Reliefs From the Temples of Sebennytos and Iseion in American Collections," *The Journal of the Walters Art Gallery*, Baltimore, Vol. VII-VIII, 1944-45, p. 49, fig. 10; *Cincinnati Art Museum Guide*, 1956, p. 10; *Ancient Civilizations*, Cincinnati, 1961, No. 9.
Collections: Kelekian, New York.

1947.372
SEATED FIGURE OF OSIRIS, XXX-XXXII Dynasties, 332-30 B.C. White marble, height $6\frac{31}{32}$ (17.7), width $1\frac{7}{8}$ (4.7), depth $2\frac{3}{4}$ (6.9).
Gift of Millard F. and Edna F. Shelt.

1947.13
CAT BOX, said to have been found at Bubastis, XXX-XXXII Dynasties, 332-30 B.C. Bronze, height $4\frac{7}{32}$ (10.7), width $1\frac{9}{16}$ (4.0), depth 4 (10.1).
Engraving on head and necklace.
Gift of Millard F. and Edna F. Shelt.

1947.69
OSIRIS, XXX-XXXII Dynasties, 332-30 B.C. Bronze, height $4\frac{1}{2}$ (11.9), width $1\frac{1}{4}$ (3.2), depth $\frac{25}{32}$ (2.0).
Standing figure with crown and plumes of Upper Egypt.
Gift of Millard F. and Edna F. Shelt.

1947.70
KHONSU, XXX-XXXII Dynasties, 332-30 B.C. Bronze, height $5\frac{3}{4}$ (14.6), width $1\frac{7}{32}$ (3.0), depth $\frac{3}{4}$ (1.9).
Seated figure with high crown of crescent, disk and plumes, flail in right hand and crook in left; long hair and beard.
Gift of Millard F. and Edna F. Shelt.

Four CAPITALS, probably from Medinet-al-Fayum, Coptic, V c A.D., limestone. Round base, quadrangular top with incurving sides, acanthus decoration.
1952.9
Height $20\frac{1}{2}$ (52.0), width of top $27\frac{1}{2}$ (69.8) of base 19 (48.2).
1952.10
Height $20\frac{1}{2}$ (52.0), width of top $24\frac{1}{2}$ (62.2) of base 18 (45.7).
1952.11
Height $13\frac{1}{2}$ (34.3), width of top $21\frac{1}{2}$ (54.6) of base 13 (33.0).
1952.12
Height 15 (38.1), width of top $21\frac{1}{2}$ (54.6) of base 15 (38.1).

1953.123
NICHE-HEAD, found at Bawit, central Egypt, Coptic, V-VI c. A.D. Limestone, height $20\frac{7}{8}$ (50.3), width $30\frac{1}{2}$ (77.5), depth ca. $12\frac{1}{2}$ (32.0).
Published: *The Art Quarterly*, XVII, 2, 1954, p. 179.
Cf. Louvre No. X 5101.

Greek, Etruscan, Roman and Hellenistic

1960.484
FEMALE FIGURE, Cycladic, said to have been found at Iraklia, ca. 2500 B.C. Marble, height 26³⁄₁₆ (66.5), width 8⁵⁄₁₆ (21.1), depth 3⁵⁄₁₆ (8.4).
Published: *The Art Quarterly*, XXIII, 4, 1960, p. 398, illustrated p. 401; "La chronique des arts," *Gazette des Beaux-Arts*, No. 1117, Feb. 1962, p. 18 illustrated; *Ancient Civilizations*, Cincinnati, 1961, No. 12; *Cincinnati Art Museum Bulletin*, VI, 1-4, July 1961, inside back cover.

1962.343
VOTIVE OBJECT (female figure?), early Bronze Age. Marble, height 2³⁄₈ (6.1), width 1³⁄₈ (3.5), depth ¼ (0.6).
Provenance not known but probably from Troy because of donors' close association with excavations of Troy where many objects of this kind were found in layers II-V. See also 1962.344, .345.
The William T. and Louise Taft Semple Collection.

1960.484

33

1962.344
VOTIVE OBJECT (female figure?), early Bronze Age. Marble, height 1 5/8 (4.1), width 1 (2.5), depth 1/4 (0.6).
Probably from Troy (see 1962.343, .345).
The William T. and Louise Taft Semple Collection.

1962.345
VOTIVE OBJECT (female figure?), early Bronze Age. Marble, height 1 7/8 (4.8), width 1 (2.5), depth 3/16 (0.5).
Probably from Troy (see 1962.343, .344).
The William T. and Louise Taft Semple Collection.

1962.392
BOAT, date uncertain but probably second millenium B.C. Bronze, height 1 1/2 (3.8), width 1 1/16 (2.7), depth 5 7/8 (14.9).
This small boat, presumably a votive offering of fairly early Eastern Mediterranean origin, exhibits peculiarities of construction for which no exact parallel has yet been found. Greece, the Aegean Islands and Crete have all been suggested as possible sources.
Published: *Cincinnati Art Museum Bulletin*, VII, 3-4, Feb. 1965, illustrated.
The William T. and Louise Taft Semple Collection.

1962.395
HORSE, ca. VIII c. B.C. Bronze, height 3 3/16 (8.1), width 2 (5.0), depth 3 7/8 (9.9).
Probably found at Olympia. Cf. 1962.396.
Published: *Cincinnati Art Museum Bulletin*, VII, 3-4, Feb. 1965, illustrated.
The William T. and Louise Taft Semple Collection.

1962.396
HORSE, ca. VIII c. B.C. Bronze, height 3 1/32 (7.7), width 7/8 (2.2), depth 1 15/16 (4.9).
Probably found at Olympia. Cf. 1962.395.
Published: *Cincinnati Art Museum Bulletin*, VII, 3-4, Feb. 1965, illustrated.
The William T. and Louise Taft Semple Collection.

1962.397
BIRD, ca. VIII c. B.C. Bronze, height 2 (5.1), width 1 3/8 (3.4), depth 1 9/16 (3.9).
Probably found at Olympia.
Published: *Cincinnati Art Museum Bulletin*, VII, 3-4, Feb. 1965, illustrated.
The William T. and Louise Taft Semple Collection.

1955.791
VOTIVE MIRROR WITH FIGURE OF ARTEMIS, Peloponnesus or Ionian Asia Minor, early VI c. B.C. Bronze, height 14 13/16 (37.6), width (Diameter of Mirror) 7 11/16 (19.5), depth 1 (2.5).
Published: *Ancient Civilizations*, Cincinnati, 1961, No. 14.
Collections: Pierpont Morgan, New York.
Gift of Michael Schaible in honor of his father.

1962.391
HEAD OF A MAN, probably from the Acropolis, Athens, late VII or early VI c. B.C. Limestone with traces of color, height 1 9/16 (3.9), width 1 1/4 (3.2), depth 1 9/16 (3.9).
Published: *Cincinnati Art Museum Bulletin*, VII, 3-4, Feb. 1965, illustrated.
The William T. and Louise Taft Semple Collection.

1962.392

1955.791

1955.791

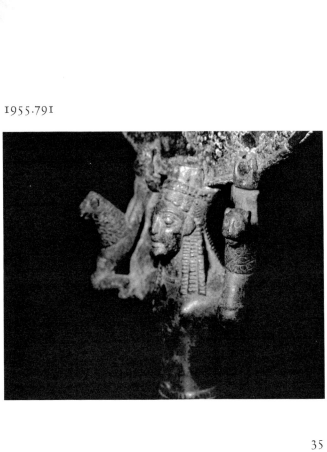

1962.390

1956.13
BULL, probably Attic, late VI c. B.C. Bronze, height 12⁵⁄₁₆ (31.3), width 4⁷⁄₁₆ (11.2), depth 15³⁄₈ (39.1). At a later date, probably in Roman times, this figure was bored to serve as a fountain.
Published: W. Froehner, *Collection Hoffman, catalogue des objets d'art antiques*, 1886, Pl. XXXVIII; Furtwängler, *Bonner Jahrbücher* 114-15, 1906, pp. 199 ff; G. M. A. Richter, *Animals in Greek Sculpture*, London, 1930, p. 22, note 3; *Cincinnati Art Museum Guide*, 1956, cover, p. 8; *Pantheon*, Munich, 1960, p. LXV; *Ancient Civilizations*, Cincinnati, 1961, No. 15.

1962.390
HEAD OF HERMES, Attic, late VI c. B.C. Marble with traces of color, height 6⁵⁄₁₆ (16.0), width 4 (10.2), depth 4¼ (10.8).
The shoulders of this bearded male head are modulated into the dressed sides of a herm. It was said to have been found at Vrona near Markopoulo, Attica.
Published: Walter H. Siple, "Two Greek Heads on Exhibition in the Museum," *Bulletin of the Cincinnati Art Museum*, II, 2, April 1931, pp. 41-47, 62; *Athenische Mitteilung* 60/62, 1935/36, p. 301, Taf. 102; *The Art Quarterly*, XXVI, 4, 1963, p. 483, illustrated, p. 487; *Cincinnati Art Museum Bulletin*, VII, 3-4, Feb. 1965, illustrated.
The William T. and Louise Taft Semple Collection.

1901.28
TITYROS, Boeotia, VI c. B.C. Pottery, height 4¼ (10.8), width 1⁷⁄₁₆ (3.7), depth ⅞ (2.3).
Published: Paul Baur, "Tityros," *American Journal of Archaeology*, Second Series, IX, 1905, pp. 157-165, illustrated, p. 158, fig. 1.
Gift of Dr. Paul V. C. Baur.

1956.13

1957.467, .468
PAIR OF DOE'S HEAD FINIALS, region of
Sybaris, South Italy, ca. 400 B.C. Gold on bronze,
(1957.467) height 7⁷⁄₁₆ (18.8), width 1¾ (4.5),
depth 2¼ (5.8), weight 440 grams, (1957.468)
height 7½ (19.0), width 1¹³⁄₁₆ (4.6), depth 2³⁄₁₆ (5.6),
weight 442.5.
Published: *The Art Quarterly*, XXII, 1, 1959, p. 78,
illustrated. p. 79; *Pantheon*, Munich, 1960,
illustrated p. LXVI; *Ancient Civilizations*,
Cincinnati, 1961, No. 22.

1962.389
HEAD OF A WOMAN, Attic, late IV c. B.C.
Marble, height 8⅞ (22.5), width 5⁹⁄₁₆ (14.1), depth 6¾
(17.1).
Remains of large fingers on the head have led some
scholars to suggest that it is a fragment from a
Battle of Centaurs and Lapithae. Others believe
that the air of gentle resignation shows its
origin on a grave stela.
Published: Walter H. Siple, "Two Greek Heads on
Exhibition in the Museum," *Bulletin of the Cincinnati
Art Museum*, II, 2, Apr. 1931, pp. 41-47;
Cincinnati Art Museum Bulletin, VII, 3-4, Feb. 1965,
cover; *The Art Quarterly*, XXVII, 2, 1964,
p. 203, illustrated p. 207.
The William T. and Louise Taft Semple Collection.

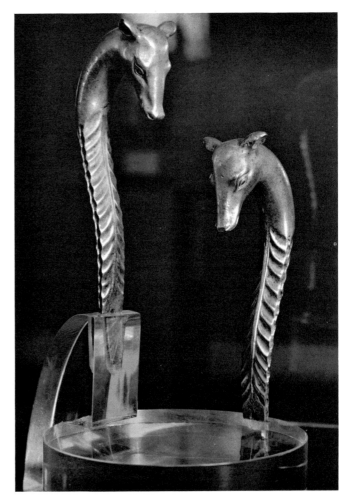

1962.389

1962.389

1962.416
LOUTROPHOROS, Attic, IV c. B.C. Marble
with traces of polychromy, height 53¼ (135.3),
width of wings 16⅛ (40.9), diameter of vase 13⁵⁄₁₆
(33.8), of cap 16¹⁵⁄₁₆ (43.0).
The loutrophoros was the pottery vessel from
which the bridal bath was poured. When placed on
a grave mound, and sometimes executed in
marble, it signified the burial of an unmarried
person. Few complete marble loutrophoroi have
survived and this may be the only one in America.
Published: Francis W. Robinson, "An Unpublished
Loutrophoros or Greek Sepulchral Urn," *Bulletin of
the Cincinnati Art Museum*, v, 1, Jan. 1934,
pp. 2-11; *Ancient Civilizations*, Cincinnati, 1961,
No. 18; *Cincinnati Art Museum Bulletin*, VII, 3-4,
Feb. 1965, illustrated.
The William T. and Louise Taft Semple Collection.

1962.416

1962.416

1946.40
LION, Attic, late IV c. B.C. prior to sumptuary
law of Demetrius Phalereus. Pentelic marble,
height 33¼ (84.5), width 15¾ (40.0), depth
76¾ (195.0), base height 3⅛ (8.0), width 18½ (47.0),
depth 82½ (209.5).
Published: *Cincinnati Art Museum Guide,* 1956,
p. 9; *Ancient Civilizations,* Cincinnati, 1961, No. 17;
Cornelius Vermeule and Penelope von Kersburg,
"Appendix: Lions, Attic and Related," *American
Journal of Archaeology,* Apr. 1968, p. 100.
Vermeule and Kersburg date this 350-340 B.C.

1945.66
HEAD OF A YOUNG WOMAN, Kalkis,
IV-III c. B.C. Pentelic marble, height 13½ (34.3),
width 9³⁄₁₆ (23.4), depth 8¾ (22.2).
This idealized head with hair veiled was almost
certainly socketed into a sepulchral figure of less
precious stone. The marked softness and
refinement of the modeling indicates an awareness
of the work of both Praxiteles and Skopas on
the part of the sculptor.
Published: Otto J. Bendel, "A Fourth Century Greek
Head of a Young Woman," *The Art Quarterly,*
VI, I, 1943, p. 3, fig. 7, footnote 19.
Collections: Brummer, New York.

1946.40

1945.66

1957.504
ASKLEPIOS, Attic, early III c. B.C. Bronze,
height 9⅜ (23.8), width 3⅛ (8.0), depth 1¹³⁄₁₆ (4.6).
Published: Salomon Reinach, *Répertoire de la
statuaire grecque et romaine,* 6:11, fig. 1, Paris,
Librairie Ernest Leroux, 1930; Dr. Margarete Bieber,
"A Bronze Statuette in Cincinnati and Its Place in the
History of the Asklepios Types," *Proceedings of the
American Philosophical Society,* Vol. 101, No. 1,
Feb. 1957, p. 70 and fig. 104, p. 71; *The Art
Quarterly,* XXI, 1, 1958, p. 83, illustrated;
Dr. Margarete Bieber, *The Sculpture of the Hellenistic
Age,* New York, Columbia University Press,
revised edition, 1961, p. 180, fig. 779-781; *Ancient
Civilizations,* Cincinnati, 1961, No. 19.
Exhibited: Sambon Exposition.
Collections: Jameson, Paris.
Gift of Michael Schaible in honor of his father.

1946.9
HEIFER, Attic, III c. B.C. Parian marble, height 19⅞
(50.4), width 11¾ (29.9), depth 51½ (130.9).
This marble copy of Myron's fifth-century bronze
that stood on the Acropolis, or the Pnyx, was
found in the ruins of a Roman collector's villa at
Anzio together with the *Fanciulla d'Anzio* in the
Museo Nazionale delle Terme, Rome. It is
supported by a wall along its right flank instead of
being underpinned in the usual manner. Dr. Georg
Karo remarked that this feature was unique in his
experience and in an address (unpublished) to the
Spring Meeting of the Classical Association of
the Midwest and South, Cincinnati 1946, said,
"Once when we wanted to know what Myron's
Heifer looked like we looked at the twenty inch
bronze in the Bibliotheque Nationale. Now we
must look at the Cincinnati marble."
Published: *Art News,* Summer 1957, illustrated p. 45;
Cincinnati Art Museum Guide, 1956, p. 9;
Ancient Civilizations, Cincinnati, 1961, No. 16.
Exhibited: *Masterpieces of Sculpture,* Minneapolis
Institute of Arts, 1949.

1946.9

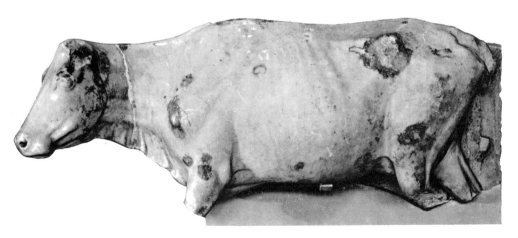

1946.9

1966.4

1966.4
APHRODITE ANADYOMENE, Alexandria,
II c. B.C. Marble, height 12⅞ (32.7), width 6⁷⁄₁₆ (16.3),
depth 3¾ (9.5).
Published: *The Art Quarterly*, XXIX, 3-4, 1966,
p. 289, illustrated p. 292; "La Chronique des arts,"
Gazette des Beaux-Arts, No. 1176, Paris, Feb. 1967,
p. 141; *Cincinnati Art Museum Bulletin*, VIII, 2-3,
Jan. 1968, illustrated p. 34.
Gift of Lucien Wulsin.

1966.5
HEAD OF A FAUN, probably from Western
Asia Minor, III-I c. B.C. Marble, height 9⅝ (24.5),
width 7 (17.8), depth 7⅝ (19.4).
The Faun of Vienne, Roman copy of a Hellenistic
sculpture of the III to I century B.C., in the Louvre,
may be based on this. Parts of the body and other
fragments survive in the Louvre figure, suggesting
that the faun was seated holding an infant Dionysus,
or stood near a nymph in a composition sometimes
called "Invitation to the Dance."
Published: *The Art Quarterly*, XXIX, 3-4, 1966,
p. 289, illustrated p. 291; "La chronique des arts,"
Gazette des Beaux-Arts, Feb. 1967, p. 56,
No. 214; *Cincinnati Art Museum Bulletin*, VIII, 2-3,
Jan. 1968, p. 33.
Gift of Mr. and Mrs. John J. Emery.

1966.5

1884.193

1906.40
WARRIOR, Etruscan, VI-V c. B.C. Bronze,
height 10⁷⁄₁₆ (26.5), width 3½ (8.9), depth 3⅝ (9.2).
Published: *Cincinnati Art Museum Guide*, 1956, p. 3;
*University of Cincinnati Executive Management
Program*, College of Business Administration, 1960;
Ancient Civilizations, Cincinnati, 1961, No. 23;
Masterpieces of Etruscan Art, Worcester Art Museum,
No. 42, p. 54, illustrated p. 143.
Exhibited: *Small Bronzes of the Ancient World*, The
Detroit Institute of Arts, March 5-April 21, 1947;
Masterpieces of Etruscan Art, Worcester Art Museum,
Apr. 21-June 4, 1967.
Gift of William Baer.

1884.193
CINERARY URN AND COVER, Etruscan, III c.
B.C. Terra cotta with traces of original colored glaze,
Cover: height 5⁷⁄₁₆ (13.9), width 18½ (47.0), depth 10⅝
(26.9), Urn: height 10⁷⁄₁₆ (26.5), width 17 (43.2),
depth 9⅛ (23.3).
Heavy rectangular box with battle of Polyneices
and Eteocles depicted in relief on one side; cover
surmounted by a woman reclining with head
resting on a pillow.
Published: *Ancient Civilizations*, Cincinnati,
1961, No. 24.
Gift of the Woman's Art Museum Association.

1902.7
FRAGMENT OF SARCOPHAGUS, Roman,
II c. A.D. Marble, height 7⅞ (20.0), width 8⁵⁄₁₆ (21.1),
depth 9⅝ (24.5).
Entered the Museum's collection as the base for
Moses Ezekiel's bronze bust, "Ecce Homo."
Gift of Harry M. Levy and George W. Harris.

1906.40

1957.485

PORTRAIT HEAD OF A MAN, Rome,
Republican period, II-I c. B.C. Marble, height 18 (45.7),
width 7⅞ (20.1), depth 8⅟₁₆ (20.5).
Published: *The Art Quarterly*, XXI, 1, 1958, pp. 82, 83;
Ancient Civilizations, Cincinnati, 1961, No. 25.
Gift of William H. Chatfield.

1969.824

HEAD OF THE EMPEROR CLAUDIUS
AS A BOY, Roman, I c. A.D. Marble, height
11¼ (28.6), width 7⁵⁄₁₆ (18.6), depth 8 (20.3).
Given in memory of Delia Workum Striker by
Dr. Cecil Striker, Dr. Theodore W. Striker and
Professor Cecil L. Striker.

1969.824

1957.485

1946.5

1968.112

1946.5
PORTRAIT HEAD OF A WOMAN, Rome, ca. 195 A.D. Fine-grained Italian marble, height 9¹³⁄₁₆ (25.0), width 9⁵⁄₁₆ (25.2), depth 9½ (24.0).

The Near Eastern style of the subject's hair suggests that this may have been a portrait of Julia Domna, wife of the Emperor Septimius Severus, or of one of Julia's daughters.

Published: *Cincinnati Art Museum Guide*, 1956, p. 7; *Ancient Civilizations*, Cincinnati, 1961, No. 27; George M. A. Hanfmann, *Roman Art: A Modern Survey of the Art of Imperial Rome*, New York Graphic Society, Greenwich, Conn., 1964, No. 84, pp. 97-8, 179; Cornelius C. Vermeule, "Greek and Roman Portraits in North American Collections Open to the Public: A Survey of Important Monumental Likenesses in Marble and Bronze which have not been Published Extensively," *Proceedings of the American Philosophical Society*, 108, No. 2,

p. 103; *Art of the Late Antique from American Collections*, Brandeis University, Waltham, Mass., 1968, No. 1, pl. 1; Michael Grant, *The Climax of Rome*, Weidenfeld & Nicholson, London, 1969, pl. 8. Exhibited: *Roman Art and Culture in Ancient Coins*, Fogg Art Museum, Harvard University, August 1942; *Master Works of Sculpture*, John Herron Art Institute, Indianapolis, Feb. 8-Mar. 18, 1956; *Art of the Late Antique*, Rose Art Museum, Brandeis University, Waltham, Mass., Dec. 18, 1968-Feb. 16, 1969.

1968.112
SACRED RELIEF: MITHRAS SACRIFICING THE BULL, Via Praeneste, Rome, late II c. A.D. Limestone, height 24⅝ (62.5), width 37½ (95.2), depth 7 (17.8).
Published: *Museum News*, Jan. 1969, p. 47.
Gift of Mr. and Mrs. Fletcher E. Nyce.

1958.257

TOMB PORTRAIT, Palmyra, Syria, II c. A.D.
Limestone with traces of color on background and
left side of head, height 20¾ (52-7), width 16¼ (41.48).
depth 8⅞ (22.5).
Inscribed: On background above man's left
shoulder, in Aramaic, "Malocha son of Nur-Bel, alas."
Cf. *Corpus Inscriptionum Semiticarum*, Paris 1926,
Pars II, Tomus III, Nos. 4438-4442 (probably
members of the same family).
Published: *The Art Quarterly*, XXI 4, 1958, pp. 429,
illustrated p. 428.
Gift of E. S. David.

1960.485

ARCHITECTURAL ORNAMENT WITH
HUMAN HEAD, believed to have been found at
Baalbek (Heliopolis), Lebanon, late Roman, III c. A.D.
Stone, height 4¹⁵⁄₁₆ (12.5), width 6⅛ (15.5),
depth 4⁵⁄₁₆ (11.0).
Gift of Lucien Wulsin.

1951.178

HORSE, Yemen, Himyaritic period, II c. B.C.-II c.
A.D. Bronze, height 3⅞ (9.9), width 1⁵⁄₁₆ (3.3),
depth 2¹⁵⁄₁₆ (7.5).
Inscribed: Sabaean characters, not yet translated.
Exhibited: University Museum Television program,
What in the World?, Oct. 10, 1954, University of
Pennsylvania, Philadelphia.
Gift of Philip R. Adams.

1958.257

Fragments from the Nabataean temple complex, Khirbet Tannur, Jordan, late II c. B.C.-II c. A.D., excavated in 1937-38 by the American School of Oriental Research under the direction of Dr. Nelson Glueck.
Purchased from the American Society of Oriental Research through a fund contributed by the following:

Dr. Julian E. Benjamin, Oscar Berman, Mrs. Gilbert Bettman, Herbert R. Bloch, Milton L. Brown, A. B. Cohen, Mrs. Ivan Fischer, J. I. Fleischer, Dr. and Mrs. A. J. Freiberg, Harry A. Freiberg, Dr. Henry B. Freiberg, Mrs. J. W. Freiberg, Julius W. Freiberg, Herbert Greer French, Edgar Friedlander, Harry Glueck, Hillel Glueck, Mrs. Morris Glueck, Nathan Glueck, Mrs. Nelson Glueck, Samuel Glueck, Alva W. Goldsmith, Hugo Goldsmith, Mary Hanna, Hebrew Union College, Mrs. E. L. Heinsheimer, Max Hirsch, Charles S. Iglauer, Dr. and Mrs. Samuel Iglauer, Ben Katz, Carl J. Kiefer, Edward Kuhn, Robert Kuhn, Mrs. Simon Kuhn, Jeffrey Lazarus, Simon Lazarus, Charles J. Livingood, H. S. Livingood, Jacob W. Mack, Louis D. Marks, Henry Meiss, Leonard Minster, Rev. Dr. Julian Morgenstern, Mr. and Mrs. I. W. Oscherwitz, Rev. Dr. David Philipson, Carl E. Pritz, Dr. J. L. Ransohoff, Adolph Rosenberg, Frederick Rauh, Murray Seasongood, Mr. and Mrs. W. T. Semple, Robert Senior, Mr. and Mrs. Herman T. Shapiro, Millard Shelt, Stanley D. Simon, Albert Steiner, Mr. and Mrs. S. G. Stricker, Mrs. Mary Miller Thayer, Louis Ullman, George H. Warrington in memory of Elsie Holmes Warrington, Dr. H. B. Weiss, Irvin F. Westheimer, Leo F. Weston.

1939.279
INCENSE ALTAR. Limestone, height 7¾ (19.7), width 7 (17.7), depth 5¹⁵⁄₁₆ (15.1).
Published: Glueck, *Deities,* 1965, p. 510, pl. 192-c.
Roughly cylindrical with deep depression in the top somewhat blackened, notch out of rim of basin.

1939.291
INCENSE ALTAR. Limestone, height 4⁷⁄₁₆ (11.2), width 4¹¹⁄₁₆ (11.9), depth 2⁹⁄₁₆ (6.5).
Published: Glueck, *Deities,* 1965, pl. 193-b.
Small dressed piece of stone with notch in one side.

1939.212
CYLINDRICAL ALTAR WITH TWO WINGED NIKES IN RELIEF SEPARATED BY FLUTED PILASTERS.
Limestone, height 16¹⁄₁₆ (40.9), width 15¼ (38.8), depth 9¹¹⁄₁₆ (24.1).
Published: Glueck, *Bulletin of the Cincinnati Art Museum,* XII, 1, Jan. 1941, p. 10; Glueck, *Deities,* 1965, pp. 445-447, 464, 508-509, pl. 189-a, b.

1939.290
ALTAR. Limestone, height 7¹⁵⁄₁₆ (20.1), width 12¹⁵⁄₁₆ (32.9), depth 3⁷⁄₁₆ (8.7).
This fragment has rounded sides and rectilinear pilasters similar to 1939.212 but no vestige of Nikes.
Published: Glueck, *Deities,* 1965, p. 509, pl. 191-c.

1939.223
EAST FACADE OF THE ALTAR-BASE, Period II. Limestone, height 100³⁄₁₆ (254.5), width 91¾ (233.0), depth 15⅜ (39.0).
The heart of the shrine of Khirbet-Tannur was an Altar raised on a box-like podium. When the original Altar-Base became dilapidated, it was encased in a second structure shortly before 7 B.C. of which this arch decorated the east and most important side and framed the remains of Altar-Base I. In Period III, a third Altar-Base was built in like manner around the first two with the Period II arch framed by the decorated pilasters (see 1939.227) of Altar-Base III, and a figure of Zeus-Hadad (1939.224) and probably one of Atargatis (see 1939.218 and .287) were set up in front of the arch. The Altar on top of the podium (see 1939.250) in each period probably approximated a miniature version of the Altar-Base. Illustrated p. 63.
Published: Glueck, *Jordan,* 1940, p. 184, fig. 110, 118; *Bulletin of the Cincinnati Art Museum,* XII, 1, Jan. 1941, pp. 4, 6, cover illustrated; *Deities,* 1965, pp. 87, 90, 102-106, 121-123, 126, 138, 146, Pl. 101, 103, 104, 105-b. Plan B p. 623-624, Plan C p. 625-626.

1939-234
BASE OF AN ALTAR. Limestone, height 4⁷⁄₁₆ (11.3), width 7⅜ (18.7), depth 7 (17.7).
A four-legged base with the vestige of a small column at each corner to support the incense basin.
Published: Glueck, *Deities,* 1965, p. 511, Pl. 193-a.

1939.209 a-b
ARCHITRAVE DECORATED WITH HEAD
OF MEDUSA. Limestone, height 11⅝₆ (29.3),
width a) 21¹⁵⁄₁₆ (55.7), b) 16½ (42.0), depth 7⅞ (19.0).
Published: Glueck, *Deities*, 1965, pp. 353, 355,
429, Pl. 38-a.

1939.258 a-b
ARCHITRAVE (in two pieces). Limestone,
height 10¼ (26.0), width a) 20⅛ (51.2), depth a) 9⁵⁄₁₆
(23.5), width b) 25⅛ (63.8), depth b) 9⁵⁄₁₆ (23.5).

1939.210 a-c
ARCHITRAVE WITH BUSTS OF
ATARGATIS (in three pieces). Limestone,
height 10¼ (26.0), width a) 16¾ (42.5), depth a) 7¹⁵⁄₁₆
(20.1), width b) 18½ (46.9), depth b) 7⁷⁄₁₆ (18.9),
width c) 15¹⁵⁄₁₆ (40.3), depth c) 10 (25.5).
Two rosettes in the center and, at each end, a bust

probably of Atargatis as the Dolphin Goddess. This
piece served as the lintel over a niche in the facade of
the pylon gateway of Period III on the east side of
the inner temple enclosure. Cf. Glueck,
Jordan, 1940, fig. 113.
Published: Glueck, *American Journal of Archaeology*,
XLI, 1937, pp. 366, 369, illustrated p. 367; *Bulletin of
the Cincinnati Art Museum*, XII, 1, Jan. 1941, p. 4;
Glueck, *Deities*, 1965, pp. 145-146, 226, Pl. 12-b,
Plan B p. 623.
Exhibited: *Land of the Bible*, Metropolitan Museum
of Art, New York, May-Dec. 1953.

1939.227
ATARGATIS AS GRAIN GODDESS.
Limestone, height 10¹⁵⁄₁₆ (27.8), width 16½ (42.0),
depth 12 (30.5).
This block from the south corner pilaster of the east
facade of the Period III Altar-Base is decorated in

high relief with the head of Atargatis, the paramount goddess of Khirbet Tannur, as Grain Goddess, set in a rosette with a stalk of wheat. There were six such representations of Atargatis, alternately as Grain Goddess and as Dolphin Goddess, (see 1939.238 below) on each corner pilaster. The pilaster was tied to the facade by a quarter-column, part of which is attached to this piece, decorated with acanthus leaves and vines. 1939.255 probably adjoins this piece completing the quarter-column and carrying the relief decoration onto the facade.
Published: Glueck, *American Journal of Archaeology,* XLI, 1937, illustrated p. 374; *Jordan,* 1940, p. 184, fig. 117; *Bulletin of the Cincinnati Art Museum,* XII, 1, Jan. 1941, p. 4, illustrated p. 5; *Deities,* 1965, pp. 122-124, 311, 315-319, 395-369, 398, Pl. 25, 26, Plan C p. 624.
Exhibited: *Land of the Bible,* Metropolitan Museum of Art, New York, May-Dec. 1953; El Al Israel Airlines, New York, Mar. 15-Apr. 15, 1959.

1939.238
ATARGATIS AS DOLPHIN GODDESS.
Limestone, height 11¼ (8.6), width 21⅛ (53.6), depth 9¼ (23.6).
Another of the six heads of Atargatis from the southeast corner pilaster of Altar Base III (see 1939.227 above). The dentilated trim at her neckline seems to identify her as Dolphin Goddess. The attached quarter-column is here decorated with vine leaves.
Published: Glueck, *Deities,* 1965, pp. 122, 146, 316, 317, 319, Pl. 27-b.

1939.215
UNFINISHED HEAD OF ATARGATIS.
Limestone, height 18¹⁵⁄₁₆ (48.1), width 22¹⁵⁄₁₆ (58.3), depth 11¹¹⁄₁₆ (29.7).
This building block bears the roughed-out head and shoulders of a woman in deep relief. She was almost certainly to be Atargatis, probably as the Dolphin Goddess.
Published: Glueck, *Deities,* p. 510, Pl. 3-a.

1939.246
BASE FOR A PILASTER. Limestone, height 10⅝ (27.0), width 17 (43.1), depth 13⅞ (35.3).
Rectilinear block undecorated.

1939.250
CAPITAL FROM THE MAIN ALTAR, Period III. Limestone, height 13¹⁵⁄₁₆ (35.4), width 11½ (29.2), depth 8⁵⁄₁₆ (21.2).
Part of a pilaster, decorated with rosettes, and its elaborate capital with foliated volutes (see also 1939.230) and a small projecting head of the Goddess.
Published: Glueck, *Deities,* pp. 90, 91, 103, 120, 124-126, 223-224, Pl. 133-a, b.

1939.230
CORNER OF A CORINTHIAN CAPITAL.
Limestone, height 8⁵⁄₁₆ (21.1), width 12¹⁄₁₆ (30.2), depth 7⅛ (18.1).
Corner of the abacus and elaborately foliated volute.
Cf. 1939.250.
Published: Glueck, *Deities,* 1965, Pl. 174-d.

1939.241
CAPITAL OF A PILASTER. Limestone, height 10¹³⁄₁₆ (27.5), width 33¹⁄₁₆ (84.0), depth 21⅞ (55.5).
Between the two corners a piece has been broken off which may have been another horn or a head of a deity.
Published: Glueck, *Deities,* 1965, Pl. 173-a, c.

1939.250

1939.232

SMALL COLUMN. Limestone, height 9 (22.8), width 5⁷⁄₁₆ (13.8), depth 5⁷⁄₁₆ (13.8).
Capital and about half the shaft of a column that may have been the support for an incense altar or thymiaterion.
Published: Glueck, *Deities*, p. 229, Pl. 191-a.

1939.222

EAGLE AND SERPENT ON A LAUREL WREATH. Limestone, height 18⅛ (46.1), width 12¹⁵⁄₁₆ (32.9), depth 9¼ (23.5).
This eagle is associated with Zeus-Hadad in the role of Helios. The serpent is believed to be associated with the rising and setting of the sun as well as having a chthonian significance.
Published: Glueck, *Bulletin of the Cincinnati Art Museum*, XII, 1, Jan. 1941, p. 7 illustrated; *Deities*, pp. 355, 444, 473, 479-484, 487-489 Pl. 140.

1939.259

HEAD OF AN EAGLE. Limestone, height 4⅛ (10.5), width 2⅛ (5.5), depth 3³⁄₁₆ (8.2).
Published: Glueck, *Deities*, p. 445, Pl. 144-a.

1939.274

ELBOW (?). Limestone, height 5⁷⁄₁₆ (13.8), width 4⅜ (11.2), depth 2⁷⁄₁₆ (6.2).
An elbow or knee, possibly of one of the many Nike figures found at Khirbet Tannur.

1939.267

FRAGMENT OF A FIGURE. Limestone, height 10¹¹⁄₁₆ (27.1), width 9½ (24.1), depth 5³⁄₁₆ (13.2).
The midsection of a human figure, probably a Nike, showing the tiered skirt and the left elbow.
Published: Glueck, *Deities*, p. 509, Pl. 190-b.

1939.262

FRAGMENT OF A FIGURE. Limestone, height 15¹⁵⁄₁₆ (40.5), width 10⁷⁄₁₆ (26.5), depth 7¹⁵⁄₁₆ (20.2).
Lower half of a human figure wearing a skirt draped after the Parthian fashion.
Published: Glueck, *Deities*, 1965, p. 250, Pl. 43-b.

1939.271

FRAGMENT OF A FIGURE. Limestone, height 8⁵⁄₁₆ (21.2), width 8¼ (20.9), depth 3⁹⁄₁₆ (9.1).
Curving grooves on one face of this piece suggest the folds of a skirt over the bulge of a knee.

1939.282

FRAGMENT OF A FIGURE. Limestone, height 5¹⁄₁₆ (12.9), width 6⅞ (17.5), depth 1⅜ (3.5).
Upper part of a human figure with the folds of a himation over the left shoulder.

1939.270

FRAGMENT OF A FIGURE. Limestone, height 9⅜ (23.8), width 11³⁄₁₆ (28.4), depth 3 (7.6).
Thin slab with curving grooves on one face representing the folds of a himation.

1939.264

FRAGMENT OF AN ARMORED FIGURE. Limestone, height 9½ (24.1), width 11 (27.9), depth 3 (7.6).

1939.287

FOOT. Sandstone, height 5⅜ (13.6), width 9⁵⁄₁₆ (23.6), depth 4¹⁵⁄₁₆ (12.6).
This is probably the foot of the sandstone Atargatis that must have stood beside the Zeus-Hadad (1939.224), framed by the arch of Altar-Base II (1939.223), during Period III. The sandstone lion (1939.218) is one of the two that stood on either side of her as the bulls flank Zeus-Hadad. These are the only fragments of this figure of Atargatis that have survived.
Published: Glueck, *Jordan*, 1940, p. 189; *Deities*, pp. 207, 270, 285, 508, Pl. 161-b.

1939.275

FOOT. Limestone, height 1¾ (4.4), width 1¾ (4.5), depth 3¹⁄₁₆ (7.7).
Published: Glueck, *Deities*, 1965, Pl. 186-d.

1939.251 and .286

FOOT AND LEG. Limestone, height 9¹⁷⁄₃₂ (24.2), width 2²³⁄₃₂ (6.9), depth 5¹¹⁄₁₆ (14.4).
Published: Glueck, *Deities*, 1965, p. 508, Pl. 186-a.

1939.283

FRAGMENT OF HAIR OR FEATHERS. Limestone, height 4¾ (12.0), width 3⁹⁄₁₆ (9.0), depth 1¹⁄₁₆ (2.7).

1939.284

FRAGMENT OF HAIR. Limestone, height 1²⁷⁄₃₂ (4.7), width 4⁹⁄₁₆ (11.1), depth 1⁹⁄₁₆ (3.9).

1939.273
FRAGMENT OF A WING. Limestone, height $6\frac{1}{2}$ (16.5), width $3\frac{7}{8}$ (9.8), depth $3\frac{5}{8}$ (9.2).
Published: Glueck, *Deities,* 1965, p. 445, Pl. 144-c.

1939.252
HAND AND FOREARM. Limestone, height $4\frac{29}{32}$ (12.1), width $2\frac{1}{8}$ (5.4), depth $2\frac{3}{16}$ (5.5).
Published: Glueck, *Deities,* 1965, p. 508, Pl. 186-c.

1939.221
HEAD. Limestone, height $5\frac{5}{8}$ (14.4), width $4\frac{3}{4}$ (12.0), depth $2\frac{3}{16}$ (5.5).
Published: Glueck, *Deities,* 1965, Pl. 132-a, b.
Exhibited: Television program, *What in the World?,* University of Pennsylvania, Philadelphia, Oct. 10, 1954.

1939.253
CROWN OF HEAD AND FOREHEAD WITH WAVY HAIR. Limestone, height $6\frac{3}{8}$ (16.1), width $10\frac{15}{16}$ (27.8), depth 9 (22.8).
Published: Glueck, *Deities,* 1965, p. 227, Pl. 184-c.

1939.225
HELIOS WEARING A RADIATE CROWN. Limestone, height 22 (56.0), width $27\frac{7}{16}$ (57.0), depth $14\frac{9}{16}$ (37.0).
Head and shoulders of the sun god wearing a rayed crown and with a torch behind each shoulder probably representing the morning and evening star.
Published: Glueck, *Deities,* 1965, pp. 144, 212, 227, 288, 292, 417, 454-455, 464-468, 472, Pl. 136.
Exhibited: *Koptische Kunst/Christentum am Nil,* Villa Hügel, Essen-Bredeney, May-Aug. 1963, No. 19; Kunsthaus, Zürich, Oct. 1963-Jan. 1964, No. 13; *Frühchristliche und Koptische Kunst,* Akademie der Bildenden Künste, Vienna, Mar.- May 1964, No. 757.

1939.216
HEAD OF HERMES-MERCURY. Limestone, height $13\frac{7}{16}$ (34.1), width $10\frac{3}{16}$ (25.9), depth $8\frac{3}{8}$ (21.3).
Male head, face almost obliterated; curly hair, stylized twisted side-locks which identify him.
Published: Glueck, *Deities,* 1965, pp. 417, 429, 469, Pl. 147.
Exhibited: *Land of the Bible,* Metropolitan Museum of Art, New York, May-Dec., 1953.

1939.263
HEAD OF HERMES-MERCURY. Limestone, height $15\frac{3}{4}$ (40.0), width $15\frac{15}{16}$ (40.5), depth $11\frac{13}{16}$ (30.0).
Roughly square block with head and shoulders in relief, the face obliterated. He wears a himation over a tunic. A wand behind his left shoulder is entwined with a serpent or serpentine vine. A partially obliterated projection near the top of the wand may have been a wing.
Published: Glueck, *Deities,* 1965, pp. 196, 417, 467-468, Pl. 153-b.

1939.229
MOUTH OF A HORN OF PLENTY. Limestone, height $7\frac{1}{16}$ (17.9), width $4\frac{5}{8}$ (11.8), depth $3\frac{11}{16}$ (9.4).
The fruit-filled mouth of one of many cornucopias found represented at Khirbet Tannur, associated with the goddess Tyche and the god Dushara and signifying "giver of wealth."
Published: Glueck, *Deities,* 1965, Pl. 144-h.

1939.237
INCENSE BURNER (?). Limestone, height $8\frac{7}{16}$ (21.4), width $9\frac{3}{16}$ (23.3), depth $7\frac{5}{16}$ (18.5).
The upper part of a hollow stone box with pierced sides, made like a temple with a peaked roof. See also 1939.239 below which is probably another fragment of the same box.
Published: Glueck, *Deities,* 1965, p. 511, Pl. 192-a.

1939.239
INCENSE BURNER (?). Limestone, height $7\frac{1}{4}$ (18.5), width $4\frac{1}{16}$ (10.4), depth $1\frac{3}{16}$ (4.2).
Small slab pierced with two holes about the diameter of a pencil and one edge grooved where it was broken along another line of holes. Probably part of 1939.237 above.

1939.228
INSCRIBED ALTAR. Limestone, height $18\frac{3}{16}$ (46.4), width $8\frac{13}{16}$ (22.3), depth $8\frac{11}{16}$ (22.1).
Inscribed: in Aramaic language, Nabataean characters, (translated by Savignac) "(The altar) which Mati'a'el (the son of U) t'el gave as a thanksgiving offering."
This inscription is not dated, but is believed to have been erected just before the earthquake in the second

quarter of the second century A.D.
Published: Glueck, *Deities*, 1965, pp. 509-510,
Pl. 194-a, b.
Exhibited: El Al Israel Airlines, New York,
Mar. 15-Apr. 15, 1959.

1939.268
INSCRIBED STELA. Limestone, height 15 (38.1),
width 7⅞ (20.0), depth 5⅛ (13.0).
Inscribed: in Aramaic language, Nabataean
characters, "(The stela) which Qosmilk made for Qos
the god of Huru (the sculptor)" or "(The stela)
which Qosmilk made for Qosallah. Huru
(the sculptor)."
This stela originally had a horn on the right as well
as the left side forming a more or less
anthropomorphic figure of the god Dushara.
Published: M. R. Savignac, *Revue Biblique*, 46, 1937,
pp. 408-409; Glueck, *Deities*, 1965, pp. 7, 91,
514-516, Pl. 196, 197.

1939.269
INSCRIBED BLOCK. Limestone, height 9⅝ (24.5),
width 16½ (41.9), depth 9⅛ (23.2).
Inscribed: in Aramaic language, Nabataean
characters, in a sunken rectangular cartouche;
badly worn; four lines, of which the last is
completely obliterated,
". . . (which was) built (by) Natir'el the son of
(Zayd'e)l for the life of Hare(tat)
(King of the Nabataeans who loves) his people . . ."
Published: M. R. Savignac, *Revue Biblique*, 46, 1937,
pp. 409-410; M. R. Savignac and Starcky, *Revue
Biblique*, 64, 1957, p. 216; Glueck, *Deities*, 1965,
p. 513, Pl. 195-a, b.
Cf. the dated Netir'el inscription, Savignac, *Revue
Biblique*, 46, 1937, p. 408, Glueck, *Deities*, p. 513.

1939.272
INSCRIBED FRAGMENT. Limestone, height 5¾
(14.5), width 6⅝ (16.8), depth 3¾ (9.5).
Inscribed: in Greek capitals, "ΑΡΑΥ."
This is a small portion of a building block
preserving only a fragment of an inscription. The
first alpha is partly obliterated.
Published: Glueck, *Deities*, 1965, p. 516, Pl. 199-a.

1939.255
ACANTHUS AND VINE LEAVES. Limestone,
height 7⅞ (20.0), width 14½ (36.8), depth 9¹³⁄₁₆ (25.0).

Relief decoration from east facade and south-east
corner pilaster of the Altar-Base of Period III.
Probably adjoined 1939.227. See also 1939.247, .248,
.249, .256 below.
Published: Glueck, *Deities*, 1965, pp. 122-125,
317, Pl. 26-a.

1939.247
ACANTHUS LEAVES. Limestone, height 11⅛
(28.3), width 5⅜ (13.6), depth 4⅞ (9.9).

1939.248
ACANTHUS LEAVES. Limestone, height 9⅛
(23.1), width 6¹⁄₁₆ (15.4), depth 8⅜ (21.3).

1939.249
ACANTHUS LEAVES WITH BERRIES.
Limestone, height 11½ (29.3), width 9½ (24.1),
depth 9 (22.8).
Published: Glueck, *Deities*, pp. 122, 123, 317, Pl. 29-c.

1939.256
ACANTHUS LEAVES. Limestone, height 2⁷⁄₁₆
(6.5), width 14³⁄₁₆ (36.0), depth 9¹¹⁄₁₆ (24.7).

1939.211
VINE LEAVES. Limestone, height 25¼ (64.2),
width 11¹¹⁄₁₆ (29.6), depth 11 (28.0).
Curving surface decorated with vine leaves and
tendrils. Cf. 1939.292, .265, .238.
Published: Glueck, *Rivers*, 1959, fig. 54(c).

1939.292
VINE LEAVES AND GRAPES. Limestone,
height 8⅞ (22.6), width 7⅝ (19.3), depth 3⁹⁄₁₆ (9.0).
Fragment decorated with relief of vine leaves
and grapes. Cf. 1939.211, .238, .265.

1939.265
VINE LEAVES AND GRAPES. Limestone,
height 11½ (29.2), width 8½ (21.6), depth 7½ (19.0).
Cf. 1939.211, .238, .292.

1939.236
HEAD OF A LION. Limestone, height 14⅝ (37.1),
width 14¹¹⁄₁₆ (37.3), depth 12¹³⁄₁₆ (15.1).
Full-round head of a life-size lion.
Published: Glueck, *Jordan*, 1940, p. 194, fig. 126;
Deities, pp. 144, 286, Pl. 165-c, d.

1939.218 a-c
HEAD OF A LION. Sandstone, height 11⅝ (29.5), width 7¹¹⁄₁₆ (19.6), depth 6¹¹⁄₁₆ (17.0).
FOREPAWS OF A LION. Sandstone, height 4¼ (10.7), width 5⁷⁄₁₆ (13.7), depth 4½ (11.4).
CHEST AND FORELEGS OF A LION. Sandstone, height 7⁵⁄₁₆ (18.5), width 7¹¹⁄₁₆ (19.5), depth 4½ (11.4).
These three fragments and the sandstone foot 1939.287 are all that have been recovered of the Atargatis figure with her two attendant lions which probably stood beside Zeus-Hadad (1939.223) in front of the Altar-Base in Period III.
Published: Glueck, *Jordan*, 1940, p. 189; *Deities*, 1965, pp. 207, 270, 285, Pl. 161-a, b.

1939.220
LION'S PAW. Limestone, height 5¼ (13.4), width 7³⁄₁₆ (18.3), depth 8 (20.3).
Published: Glueck, *Deities*, 1965, p. 270, Pl. 162-b.
Fragment of a nearly life-size lion in high relief.

1939.293
HIND LEGS AND TAIL OF A LION. Limestone, height 16¹⁵⁄₁₆ (43.0), width 7¾ (19.7), depth 8⅞ (22.6).
Published: Glueck, *Deities*, 1965, p. 270, Pl. 162-a.

1939.289
MOLD. Limestone, H 13³⁄₁₆ (33.5), width 4¾ (12.1), depth 4³⁄₁₆ (10.1).
Stone billet with star-shape cut deeply into one end.
Published: Glueck, *Deities*, 1965, p. 227, Pl. 191-d.

1939.240
CORNICE MOLDING. Limestone, height 8¾ (22.3), width 14 (35.6), depth 3 (7.7).
Egg-and-dart molding and large rosettes.

1939.257
CORNICE MOLDING. Limestone, height 11 (28.0), width 17½ (44.5), depth 15¾ (40.0).
Egg-and-dart, dentil and leaf-motif molding.

1939.285
INTERLACE MOLDING. Limestone, height 7⅛ (18.1), width 8⅞ (22.6), depth 3⅛ (7.9).
Face of a pilaster with band of decorative interlace in relief.

1939.288
SCROLLED MOLDING. Limestone, height 7⁹⁄₁₆ (19.2), width 6⁹⁄₁₆ (16.7), depth 3 (7.6).
Fragment of building block with smooth curving surface decorated with a band of scrolled or foliate forms in high relief.

1939.226
WINGED NIKE. Limestone, height 21⁷⁄₁₆ (54.5), width 13³⁄₁₆ (33.5), depth 10⁵⁄₁₆ (26.2).
Rectangular block with high relief of winged figure standing on a globe, vestiges of a palm branch in her left hand, a bannered wreath in her right. The globe probably signifies the heavens, but may also stand for the sacred mountain top. The number of these Nike blocks found suggests that they may have formed a frieze of Nikes on one of the walls. See below 1939.214, .219, .260, .261.
Published: Glueck, *Deities*, 1965, pp. 431, 445-446, 450-451, 508, Pl. 180.

1939.214
WINGED NIKE. Limestone, height 22¼ (56.5), width 13⁵⁄₁₆ (33.8), depth 9⅞ (25.0).
Rectangular block with partially obliterated relief of winged figure with vestiges of a palm branch in her left hand, a wreath in her right.
Published: Glueck, *Deities*, 1965, pp. 445, 447, Pl. 181-a.

1939.219
HEAD OF A NIKE. Limestone, height 7⁷⁄₁₆ (18.9), width 5½ (14.0), depth 4⅝ (11.8).
Probably from a Nike in high relief on a block like 1939.214, .226, .260, .261.
Published: Glueck, *Deities*, 1965, pp. 445, 450, Pl. 183-d, e.

1939.260
WINGED NIKE. Limestone, height 21⅝ (55.0), width 16⅛ (41.0), depth 6⁵⁄₁₆ (16.0).
Rectangular block with almost obliterated relief of

winged Tyche-Nike carrying a cornucopia and possibly a palm branch.
Published, Glueck, *Deities,* 1965, pp. 410, 445, 450, Pl. 182-b.

1939.261
WINGED NIKE. Limestone, height 20 13/16 (52.4), width 14 5/8 (37.2), depth 11 5/8 (29.5).
Rectangular block with partially obliterated relief of a Nike wearing a tiered skirt and carrying a palm or torch or cornucopia in her right hand and garlanded wreath in her left.
Published: Glueck, *Deities,* 1965, pp. 445, 451. Pl. 182-a.

1939.217
MIDSECTION OF A NIKE. Limestone, height 13 5/16 (33.8), width 8 1/16 (20.5), depth 3 9/16 (9.1).
Front half of tiered skirt and waistline, possibly detached from a block like 1939.214, .226, .260 and .261.
Published: Glueck, *Deities,* 1965, p. 509, Pl. 190-c.

1939.280
MIDSECTION OF A NIKE. Limestone, height 5 7/8(15.0), width 8 15/16 (22.7), depth 4 3/8 (11.1).
Part of the left wing, the waistline and the top tier of the skirt of a Nike from a round altar similar to 1939.212.
Published: Glueck, *Deities,* 1965, p. 509, Pl. 190-a.

1939.231
HEAD OF A NIKE. Limesone, height 7 5/8 (19.4), width 3 31/32 (10.1), depth 5 1/4 (13.3).
Published: Glueck, *Deities,* 1965, pp. 449, 469, Pl. 183-a, b.

1939.281
FRAGMENT OF PINE-CONE (?). Limestone, height 4 11/16 (11.8), width 2 1/4 (5.7), depth 2 13/16 (7.1).

1939.242
SCEPTRE. Limestone, height 14 1/8 (35.9), width 1 7/16 (3.6), depth 1 7/16 (3.6).
Found near the sandstone figure of Zeus-Hadad (1939.224); may have been held in his right hand which is now missing.
Published: Glueck, *Deities,* 1965, pp. 203, 288, Pl. 186-a.

1939.277
HORNED STELA. Limestone, height 7 3/8 (18.7), width 8 7/8 (22.6), depth 3 7/8 (9.9).
Probably the remains of an anthropomorphic Dushara stela (cf. 1939.268). 1939.276 below appears to be the base for this stela.
Published: Glueck, *Deities,* 1965, p. 91, Pl. 198-a, b.

1939.276
BASE OF HORNED STELA. Limestone, height 6 1/16 (15.4), width 7 13/16 (19.8), depth 5 1/8 (13.1).
Published: Glueck, *Deities,* 1965, Pl. 198-c, d.
See 1939.277 above.

1939.233
BUST OF TYCHE CROWNED WITH THE ZODIAC. Limestone, height 11 5/8 (29.5), width 14 (35.6), depth 5 1/4 (13.3). Dated March 23, A.D. 5, by Prof. William Stahlman, University of Wisconsin, on the basis of the Zodiac crown which constitutes a schematic representation of the positions of various planets and constellations on that date.
Relief of a female figure with a crown suggesting the turreted walls of a city, and a veil or hood over the crown. By her right ear is a cresent moon. Behind her left shoulder is a wand tipped with a crescent bound to another wand which may represent a torch. She is encircled by a compartmented band bearing the signs of the Zodiac reading clockwise on the right, counter-clockwise on the left. This is part of a large relief of a Nike supporting this disk over her head, the caryatid Nike being in Jordan in a private collection.
Published: Glueck, *Jordan,* 1940, p. 191, fig. 122; *Bulletin of the Cincinnati Art Museum,* XII, 1, Jan. 1941, pp. 8, 10, illustrated p. 9; *Bulletin of the American Schools of Oriental Research,* No. 126, Apr. 1952, pp. 5-10, illustrated pp. 8-9; *Rivers,* 1959, illustrated fig. 51; *Deities,* 1965, pp. 92, 284, 315, 338, 383, 395-400, 412-449, Pl. 46, 48; H. P. L'Orange, *Studies on the Iconography of Cosmic Kinship,* 96, fig. 68.
Exhibited: *Land of the Bible,* Metropolitan Museum of Art, New York, May-Dec. 1953; *Koptische Kunst/Christentum am Nil,* Villa Hügel, Essen-Bredeney, May-Oct. 1963, No. 18; Zürich, Oct. 1963-Jan. 1964, No. 12; *Frühchristliche und Koptische Kunst,* Akademie der Bildenden Künste, Vienna, Mar. 11-May 3, 1964, No. 756; *L'art Copte,* Petit Palais, Paris, June-Sept. 1964, No. 10.

1939.233

1939.223 and 1939.224

1939.224

ZEUS-HADAD. Sandstone, height 45⁵⁄₁₆ (114.5), width 26 (66.0).

Seated figure wearing chiton, himation and a lion-terminal torque, he holds a thunderbolt in his left hand and his upraised right hand (broken off) may have held the limestone sceptre (1939.242) found near him. A small bull stands on either side of him by his feet. This figure and probably one of Atargatis (see 1939.287, .218) dating from Period III stood in front of the Altar-Base framed by the Period II arch (1939.223).

Published: Glueck, *American Journal of Archaeology*, XLI, 1937, p. 370, figs. 9, 10; *Jordan*, 1940, p. 186, fig. 119; *Bulletin of the Cincinnati Art Museum*, XII, No. 1, Jan. 1941, pp. 6, 8, cover illustrated; *Rivers*, 1959, fig. 29; "Nabataean Torques," *The Biblical Archaeologist*, XXV, No. 2, May 1962, pp. 57, 58, 62; *Deities*, 1965; pp. 155, 195-209, 269-270, 283-288, 395, 468, 496, 507, P. 41, 42; *Guide*, 1956, p. 11.

1939.235

HEAD OF ZEUS-HADAD. Limestone, height 8⁷⁄₁₆ (21.4), width 6¼ (15.9), depth 3⁵⁄₈ (9.2).
Small head with curly hair and beard of Parthian type.

Published: Glueck, *Jordan*, 1940, p. 189, fig. 120; *Deities*, 1965, pp. 197-198, Pl. 130.

1939.213

HEAD OF ZEUS-HADAD. Limestone, height 20½ (52.1), width 21¾ (55.3), depth 12⅝ (32.0).
Rectangular block with head and shoulders of the god in high relief. The face is completely eroded away. There appears to be the vestige of a thunderbolt behind his left shoulder.

Published: Glueck, *Deities*, 1965, pp. 395, 468, 470, 471, Pl. 41, 154-a, b; *Cincinnati Magazine*, I, 3, Dec. 1967, p. 49.

The Near East

1957.33

1957.33

KNEELING HERO BOUND WITH
SERPENTS, Tello (ancient Lagash), ca. 2800 B.C.
Alabaster, height 11¹³⁄₁₆ (30.1), width 6³⁄₁₆ (15.7),
depth 6 (15.2).
Published: A. Parrot, *Tello*, Paris, Abin Michel,
1948, p. 49, pl. III a, b, c; H. Frankfort, review of
Tello, Journal of Near Eastern Studies, VIII,
Jan.-Oct. 1949, p. 60; A. Parrot, "L'Homme aux
serpents," extrait de la revue *Syria*, XXVIII, 1951,
fasc. 1-2, pl. V; "La chronique des arts," *Gazette des
Beaux-Arts*, Jan. 1960, p. 29, No. 97; *Near Eastern
Art*, Cincinnati, 1962, fig. 1.
Collections: Géjou.

1956.14

1957.32

1969.86
HORNED ANIMAL, Anatolian, second half of
third millenium B.C. Bronze, height 2¹⁵⁄₁₆ (7.5), width
1⁷⁄₁₆ (3.6), depth 2⁷⁄₁₆ (6.2).
Cf. the larger Bull Standard, Archaeological Museum,
Ankara, No. 11850.
Given in memory of William Harry Gothard by
his friends.

1957.32
VOTIVE CALF, ca. 2300 B.C. Bronze, height 11¼
(28.6), plus overhang of tail ³⁄₁₆ (0.5), width 3¹⁵⁄₁₆ (10.0),
depth 9¹⁵⁄₁₆ (25.3).
The tail of this unusually large Sumerian bronze was
designed to swing freely in its socket. The eyes
were probably inlaid.
Published: *Near Eastern Art, Cincinnati,* 1962, No. 2.

1956.14
EMACIATED RELIGIOUS FIGURE, Larsa,
Old Babylonian, Reign of Apilsin, 1830-1813 B.C.
Bronze, height (with base) 5⅞ (14.9), height of figure
4¹⁄₁₆ (10.3), width 2⅜ (6.0), depth 3¹¹⁄₁₆ (9.3), weight
773 grams.
Published: *Archaeology,* X, 3, Sept. 1957, p. 223;
Near Eastern Art, Cincinnati, 1962, No. 3; Edith
Porada, "An Emaciated Male Figure of Bronze in the
Cincinnati Art Museum," *Studies Presented to
A. Leo Oppenheim,* The Oriental Institute of the
University of Chicago, 1964, pp. 159-166.

1958.520
PORTRAIT HEAD, Azerbaijan, ca. 1800 B.C.
Bronze, height 5⅞ (15.0), width 4¹³⁄₁₆ (12.2), depth
4½ (11.5).
This portrait head of a Semitic vizier is said to have
been found with the life-size bronze portrait head of
his non-Semitic king, now in the collection of the
Metropolitan Museum in New York (47.100.80), a
few miles south of Lake Urumia in Azerbaijan.
Published: Stanley Casson, "Achaemenid Sculpture,"
Survey of Persian Art, 1939, 1966, p. 356, pl. 107-a
and b; Pope, *Masterpieces*, 1945, p. 39, pl. 23;
Cincinnati Art Museum Bulletin, VI, 1-4, July 1961;
L. Vanden Berghe, *Archéologie de l'Iran ancien*,
Leyden, Brill, 1959, 1966, pp. 110, 278, pl. 137-b.
Exhibited: *Persian Art*, Burlington House, London,
1931, No. 19; *Persian Art*, New York, 1940, Gallery XI,
Case 5, No. 6.
Collections, Brummer; Kevorkian, New York.

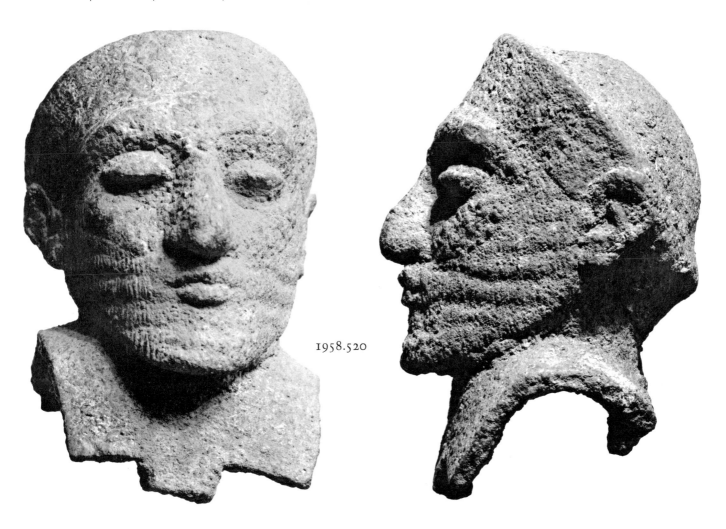

1958.520

1957.29
BREAST PLAQUE OR BELT APPLIQUE,
Luristan, probably from Kuh-i-Dasht, 1100-800 B.C.
Silver, height 4⅝ (11.75), width 10⅛ (25.72).
The repoussé design showing a sunrise ceremony has
been variously interpreted by scholars as representing
El (The Great God) giving birth to the Gemini
surrounded by priests and palm trees, or as Zurvan
giving birth to Ahuramazda and Ahriman.
Published: Phyllis Ackerman, "The Gemini Are
Born," *Archaeology*, VIII, 1, March 1955, pp. 26-30,
fig. 1; Phyllis Ackerman, "A Luristan Illustration of a
Sunrise Ceremony," *Cincinnati Art Museum
Bulletin*, V, 2, Oct. 1957, pp. 5-7; Roman Ghirshman,
"Notes Iraniennes VIII les bronzes du Luristan,"
Artibus Asiae, XXI, (Separatum), 1958, p. 37, fig. 2;
Ghirshman, *Parthian and Sasanian Dynasties*, 1962,
pp. 7, 8, fig. 11; *7000 ans d'art en Iran, Paris*, 1961,
No. 282, p. 50, pl. XIX; Ghirshman, *Ancient Iran*,
1964, p. 52, fig. 64; Culican, *Medes and Persians*,
1965, p. 27; *Bulletin of the Cleveland Museum of
Art*, Feb. 1966, pp. 42-44; Burchard Brentjes, *Die

Iranische Welt vor Mohammed, Koehler & Amaland,
Leipzig, 1967, illustrated. Pl. 26, p. 46; *Dictionnaire
universel de l'art et des artistes*, Hazan, Paris, 1967,
Vol. II, illustrated p. 424; J. Hutchison, *Paths of
Faith*, McGraw-Hill, New York, 1969, p. 312;
Leroy A. Campbell, *Mithraic Iconology and Ideology*,
Brill, Leiden, 1968, pp. XXII, 126-128, fig. 8.
Exhibited: *7000 ans d'art en Iran*, Paris, 1961, No. 282.

1957.225
CEREMONIAL CAULDRON, Luristan,
1100-800 B.C. Bronze, height (overall) 12⅛ (30.8),
exclusive of handle 6 (15.2), diameter of vessel
5⅝ (14.2)..
Published: *Cincinnati Art Museum Bulletin*, V, 2,
Oct. 1957, fig. 5, p. 1; *7000 ans d'art en Iran, Paris*,
1961, No. 373, p. 64; Ghirshman, *Ancient Iran*, 1964,
p. 78, fig. 103; Goldman, *Art Quarterly*, XXVII, 3,
1964, pp. 329, 330 fig. 2, 4; Culican, *Medes and
Persians* 1965, p. 29, pl. 3.
Exhibited: *7000 ans d'art en Iran*, Paris, 1961, No. 373.

1957.225

1958.542

1958.542
CHEEKPLATES AND BIT, Luristan, 1100-800
B.C. Bronze, a) height 7⅞ (20.0), width 9¾ (24.7),
depth 1¾ (4.4); b) height 7¹³⁄₁₆ (19.8), width 9¹⁵⁄₁₆
(23.6), depth 1⅝ (4.2); bit length 8¾ (22.2).
Published: *Near Eastern Art,* Cincinnati, 1962, No. 8;
7000 ans d'art en Iran, Paris, 1961, No. 161, p. 31;
Goldman, *Art Quarterly,* XXVII, 3, 1964, p. 329,
figs. 5, 6.
Exhibited: *7000 ans d'art en Iran,* Paris, 1961.

1958.542

1954.496
CHEEK PLATE, Luristan, 1100-800 B.C. Bronze,
height 5⁹⁄₁₆ (14.1), width 5¼ (13.4), depth 1¹⁄₁₆ (2.7).
Published: *Survey of Persian Art*, 1939, 1966, pp.
258-259, 291, 860, pl. 33-A; Ackerman, *Guide to the
Exhibition of Persian Art*, New York, 1940,
p. 96 T; Pope, *Masterpieces*, 1945, p. 27, pl. 11; *In
Honor of the Shah*, Asia Institute, New York, 1949-50;
Phyllis Ackerman, "A Luristan Illustration of a
Sunrise Ceremony," *Cincinnati Art Museum Bulletin*,
v, 2, Oct. 1957, pp. 3, 5, fig. 2; *Iran Review*,
Washington, I, 2-3, 1961, p. 38; Rosa Maria Carless,
"Notes on Luristan Bronzes," *Apollo*, July 1965, p. 29.
Exhibited: Johns Hopkins University, Baltimore,
1940, No. 2; *Persian Art*, New York, 1940; *In Honor
of the Shah*, New York, 1959-60.
Collections: Pope-Ackerman.

1947.580
CHEEK PLATE, Luristan, ca. 1100-800 B.C. Bronze,
height 5⁵⁄₁₆ (13.5), width 4³⁄₁₆ (11.0), depth 1¹⁄₁₆ (2.7).
Published: *Cincinnati Art Museum News*, III, 1, Jan.
1948, illustrated p. 1; Philip R. Adams, "Sculpture
of the Middle East," *Cincinnati Art Museum
Bulletin*, I, 3, Feb. 1951, p. 4; Rosa Maria Carless,
"Notes on Luristan Bronzes," *Apollo*, July 1965, p. 30.

1954.496

1954.497

TALISMAN (The "Many-Formed Great God"),
Luristan, 1100-800 B.C. Bronze, height 7⅜ (18.8),
width 2¹¹⁄₁₆ (6.8), depth ⅞ (2.2).
Published: Ackerman, *Guide to the Exhibition of
Persian Art*, New York, 1940, p. 106, panel 3 S;
In Honor of the Shah, New York, 1949-50; Pope,
Masterpieces, 1945, p. 22, pl. 6; *Cincinnati Art
Museum Bulletin*, V, 2, Oct. 1957, p. 7; William
Culican, "Bronzes of Ancient Iran," *Annual Bulletin*,
National Gallery of Victoria, Australia, IV, 1962, p. 3,
pl. 3; E. Bacon, *Vanished Civilizations*, McGraw-Hill,
1963, p. 225, pl. 10; Culican, *Medes and Persians*, 1965,
p. 23, fig. 3; Rosa Maria Carless, "Notes on Luristan
Bronzes," *Apollo*, July 1965, p. 28.
Exhibited: *Persian Art*, New York, 1940; *In Honor
of the Shah*, New York, 1949-50.
Collections: Pope-Ackerman.

1954.498

TALISMAN (Lion avatar of The Great God),
Luristan, 1100-800 B.C. Bronze, height
4⁵⁄₁₆ (10.8), width 1⅝ (4.2), depth ¾ (2.0).
Published: Ackerman, *Guide to the Exhibition of
Persian Art*, New York, 1940, p. 102, panel 2 U;
In Honor of the Shah, New York, 1949-50.
Exhibited: *Persian Art*, New York, 1940; *In Honor of
the Shah*, New York, 1949-50.
Collections: Pope-Ackerman.

1954.499

TALISMAN (The Capricornus avatar of The
Great God), Luristan, 1100-800 B.C. Bronze, height
4¹¹⁄₁₆ (11.9), width 3⅛ (8.0), depth ⁷⁄₁₆ (1.8).
Published: Ackerman, *Guide to the Exhibition of
Persian Art*, New York, 1940, p. 95; *In Honor of the
Shah*, New York, 1949-50; Pope, *Masterpieces*, 1945,
p. 23, pl. 7; Phyllis Ackerman, "A Luristan
Illustration of a Sunrise Ceremony," *Cincinnati Art
Museum Bulletin*, V, 2, Oct. 1957, pp. 2, 3; *Iran
Review*, Washington, D. C., I, 2-3, 1961, p. 38.
Exhibited: *Persian Art*, New York, 1940; *In Honor
of the Shah*, New York, 1949-50.
Collections: Pope-Ackerman.

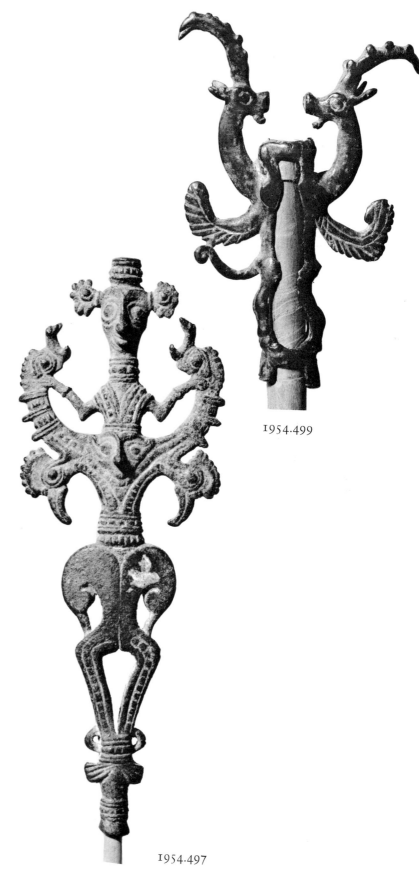

1954.499

1954.497

1961.102

1954.501
AXE HEAD, Luristan, 1100-800 B.C. Bronze, length 8⅞ (22.6), width 3¹³⁄₁₆ (9.7), depth 1½ (2.3).
Published: Ackerman, *Guide to the Exhibition of Persian Art*, New York, 1940, p. 110, panel 4 R; *In Honor of the Shah*, New York, 1949-50.
Exhibited: *Persian Art*, New York, 1940; *In Honor of the Shah*, New York, 1949-50.
Collections: A. U. Pope.

1954.500
HARNESS-RING, Luristan, 1100-800 B.C. Bronze, height 3¾ (9.4), width 3⅝ (9.2), depth 1¹⁄₁₆ (2.7).
Capricornus and Lion avatars of The Great God.

1961.146
BRACELET, Luristan, 1100-800 B.C. Bronze, diameter 2¾ (7.0), cross-section width ½ (1.2), depth (0.1), width of terminals ⅞ (2.2).
The terminals are triple horses' heads.
Gift of Dr. and Mrs. Nelson Glueck.

1955.313
BRACELET, Luristan, 1100-800 B.C. Bronze, diameter 2½ (6.3), cross-section ⅛ (0.4), width of terminal lion's head ½ (1.2).
Gift of K. Rabenou.

1961.102
ASTARTE, Southern Syria, IX-VI c. B.C. Terra cotta, height 12⅜ (31.5), width 6¼ (15.8), depth 4⅛ (10.2).
Published: Glueck, *Rivers*, 1959, p. 117, fig. 19 (opp. p. 77); *The Art Quarterly*, XXIV, 3, 1961, p. 295, illustrated p. 297; *Cincinnati Art Museum Bulletin*, VII, 3-4, Feb. 1965, illustrated.
Gift of Dr. and Mrs. Nelson Glueck.

1952.7
PRIEST IN RITUAL COSTUME, Calah, 883-859 B.C. Alabaster, height 36 (91.5), width 33½ (85.0).
Published: *Cincinnati Art Museum Bulletin*, II, 2, May 1952, illustrated p. 10; *Near Eastern Art*, Cincinnati, 1962, cover and No. 5; *Cincinnati Art Museum Bulletin*, VIII, 1, Feb. 1966, p. 20, illustrated p. 22.
Collection: Lord Wimborne.

1952.7

1953.65

1953.67 and 1963.402

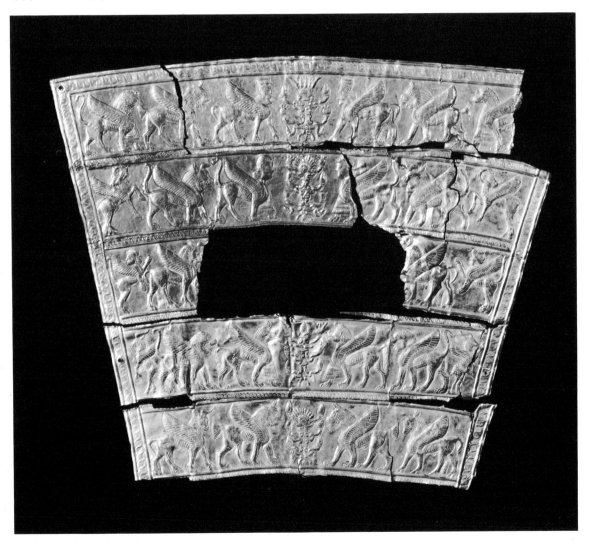

1953.67 and 1963.402
PECTORAL, Ziwiye, Kurdistan, Manaean, IX-VIII c. B.C. Gold, height 8⅜ (21.3), width of bottom 7⅛ (18.1), of top 10 (25.5), depth ca. 0.03 cm., weight 174.5 grams.
A section comprising parts of three zones in the upper right-hand corner of the pectoral (upper left to the observer) was acquired in 1953, accessions number 1953.67. It is this section which is discussed in the earlier literature. Dr. Goldman's article discusses the balance of the pectoral, accessions number 1963.402 as well as the central portion in the collection of the Royal Ontario Museum, Toronto, and the two lower zones in the collection of Joseph H. Hirshhorn.
Published: *Cincinnati Art Museum Guide,* 1956, p. 20 (1953.67 only); Kantor, *Cincinnati Art Museum Bulletin,* Oct. 1957, pp. 11, 13; Kantor, *Journal of Near Eastern Studies,* XIX, 1, Jan. 1960; p. 3, fig. 3; Winifred Needler, "Four Near Eastern Antiquities Lent by Mr. Joseph H. Hirshhorn," *Royal Ontario Museum Bulletin of the Division of Art and Archaeology,* Toronto, June 1957, No. 25, p. 10; 7000 *ans d'art en Iran,* Paris, 1961, No. 498, p. 84; Ghirshman, *Ancient Iran,* 1964, fig. 379, color; Goldman, *Art Quarterly,* XXVII, 3, 1964, fig. 1, p. 325, p. 333.
Exhibited: 7000 *ans d'art en Iran,* Paris, 1961.

1953.65
PLAQUE WITH THREE HUNTERS AND TWO LIONS, Ziwiye, IX-VIII c. B.C. Gold, height 2⅝ (6.7), width 6½ (16.5), depth (ca. 1 mm.).
Published: Kantor, *Cincinnati Art Museum Bulletin,* Oct. 1957, pp. 10, 11; Goldman, *Art Quarterly,* XXVII, 3, 1964, p. 332 fig. 9, p. 333.

1953.68
BRACELET, Ziwiye, IX-VIII c. B.C. Gold, diameter 3¹⁄₁₆ (7.8), cross-section ¼ (0.6), width of lion heads ⅜ (1.0), weight 89.5 grams.
The bracelet is made of heavy gold wire wrapped around a core and has lion-head terminals.
Published: Kantor, *Cincinnati Art Museum Bulletin,* Oct. 1957, p. 12, illustrated.

1953.64
PLAQUE WITH HUNTER AND LION, Ziwiye, IX-VIII c. B.C. Gold, height 4⁵⁄₁₆ (11.0), width of top 2⅞ (7.3), of bottom 3⅛ (7.9), depth ca. 1 mm.
Published: Kantor, *Cincinnati Art Museum Bulletin,* V, 2, Oct. 1957, pp. 8-9; Goldman, *Art Quarterly,* XXVII, 3, 1964, p. 332, fig. 10 p. 333.

1953.69
CHEST PENDANT FOR A HORSE, Ziwiye, IX-VIII c. B.C. Gold on silver, height 8 (20.3), width of bottom 3¾ (9.5), of top 2⅜ (6.0), depth 1⁷⁄₁₆ (3.6), weight 223 grams.
Cf. pendant illustrated p. 93, fig. 113 of Godard's, *The Art of Iran,* Praeger, 1965.
Published: Kantor, *Cincinnati Art Museum Bulletin,* Oct. 1957, p. 14, fig. 6 p. 15; 7000 *ans d'art en Iran,* Paris, 1961, No. 569, p. 95, pl. XLVII.
Exhibited: 7000 *ans d'art en Iran,* Paris, 1961.

1953.69

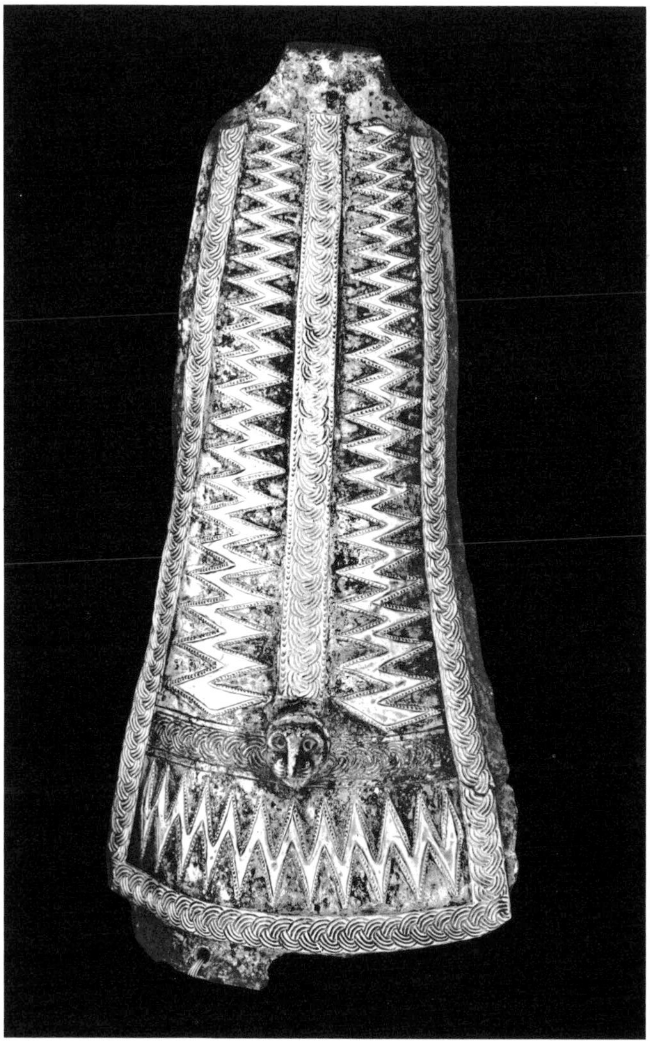

1955.70

1964.510
PLAQUE WITH TWO WINGED AND
HORNED LIONS, Ziwiye, IX-VIII c. B.C. Gold,
height 2⅛ (5.4), width 4⁵⁄₁₆ (11.0), depth ca. 1 mm.
Published: P. Amandry, *Iranica Antiqua* 6 1966 pl.
XXV a, fig. 5 pp. 120-122; *Cincinnati Art Museum
Bulletin*, VIII, 2-3, Jan. 1968, p. 35.
Gift of Mr. and Mrs. Philip R. Adams.

1955.70
ASSYRIAN PRIEST, said to have been found with
the Ziwiye treasure, 725-700 B.C. Ivory, height 7¹⁵⁄₁₆
(20.1), width 2⅝ (6.6), depth 1⅝ (4.2), weight
275 grams.
Published: *Cincinnati Art Museum Guide*, 1956,
p. 20; Kantor, *Journal of Near Eastern Studies*, XIX,
1, Jan. 1960, p. 12; *Near Eastern Art*, Cincinnati, 1962,
No. 6; Edith Porada, *Alt Iran*, Kunst der Welt,
Holle-Verlag, Baden-Baden, 1962, p. 118, illustrated
p. 120; Porada, *The Art of Ancient Iran*, Art of the
World Series, Crown, New York, 1965, pp. 124-126,
pl. 35 p. 129, color.
Gift of Mr. and Mrs. Warner L. Atkins.

1957.500
BOWL WITH RELIEF OF LIONS HUNTING
BULLS, Assyrian, VIII-VII c. B.C. Rock crystal, height
3¼ (8.4), diameter 6¹³⁄₁₆ (17.3), weight 1087 grams.
Published: *Reporter*, Bell Telephone Laboratories,
June 1961, p. 3; *Cincinnati Art Museum Bulletin*,
VI, 1-4, July 1961, illustrated; *Near Eastern Art*,
Cincinnati, 1962, No. 7; Culican, *Medes and Persians*,
1965, pl. 46; Helene J. Kantor, "A Rock Crystal Bowl
in the Cincinnati Art Museum," *Survey of Persian
Art*, XIV, 1968, pp. 2981-2993.

1957.500

1962.71

BEAKER, Amlash culture, VIII-VII c. B.C. Gold, height 8¼ (20.9), diameter of top 3⅞-4 (9.8-10.2), of bottom 2¾ (7.0), weight 234 grams.

Published: 7000 *ans d'art en Iran*, Paris, 1961, No. 76-A, pl. VI; Roman Ghirshman, "The Exposition of Iranian Art in Paris," *Archaeology*, Spring 1962, XV, 1, p. 52; *The Art Quarterly*, XXV, 3, 1962, p. 262, illustrated p. 265; Shine, *Museum News*, Feb. 1964, illustrated p. 33; Goldman, *Art Quarterly*, XXVII, 3, 1964, pp. 326-328, fig. 3; Ghirshman, *Ancient Iran*, 1964, fig. 36, color; Culican, *Medes and Persians*, 1965, p. 33, fig. 11-a; *Cincinnati Art Museum Bulletin*, VII, 3-4, Feb. 1965, illustrated; Louise Bruner, "Cincinnati: A Museum with New Walls," *Arts Magazine*, Dec. 1965, p. 37.

Exhibited: 7000 *ans d'art en Iran*, Paris, 1961.

Note: The term Amlash has been used here for convenience. Some scholars refer to this particular culture in terms of Marlik Tepe or Southwest Caspian.

1962.71

1956.82

1966.1187
BULL, Amlash, VIII-VII c. B.C. Bronze, height 3⁵⁄₁₆ (8.4), width 1⁵⁄₈ (4.1), depth 3⁷⁄₈ (9.7).
Published: *Archives of Asian Art*, XXI, 1967-68, p. 96.
Gift of Dr. and Mrs. Nelson Glueck.

1965.179
BULL, Amlash, VIII-VII c. B.C. Bronze, height 4⅛ (10.4), width 2⅛ (5.4), depth 4⁷⁄₁₆ (11.3).
Published: *Cincinnati Art Museum Bulletin*, VIII, 2-3, Jan. 1968, cover.
Bequest of Mrs. J. Louis Ransohoff.

1956.82
CUP WITH IBEX HANDLES, Hamadan, Median, VI-V c. B.C. Gold, height to top of handles 4½ (11.5), width across handles 5⅞ (14.9), diameter at rim 3¾ (9.5), weight 412 grams.
Published: *Cincinnati Art Museum Guide*, 1956, p. 19; Kantor, *Cincinnati Art Museum Bulletin*, Oct. 1957, pp. 18-19; Kantor, "A Gold Cup from Iran," *The Art Quarterly*, XX, 4, 1957, pp. 488, 491-492; Kantor, *Journal of Near Eastern Studies*, XIX, 1, Jan. 1960, p. 14; *Iran Review*, Washington, D. C., I, 2-3, 1961, illustrated p. 38; *Near Eastern Art*, Cincinnati, 1962, No. 10; *7000 ans d'art en Iran*, Paris, 1961, No. 674, p. 113, pl. LII; Ghirshman, *Ancient Iran*, 1964, pp. 96-97, fig. 125; Culican, *Medes and Persians*, 1965, pl. 27; Edith Porada, *The Art of Ancient Iran*, Crown, New York, 1965, p. 146; L. Harmond, *Histoire* (color slide set), Diffusion Hatier, Paris 1967, pp. 37, 68; B. L. Zimmerman, "Adventures in Art," *The Wonderful World of Ohio*, 32, 1, Jan. 1968, pp. 8-11, illustrated p. 10; Peter Bamm, *Alexander the Great*, McGraw-Hill, New York, 1968, p. 224 illustrated.
Exhibited: *7000 ans d'art en Iran*, Paris, 1961.
Gift of Mr. and Mrs. John J. Emery.

1958.519
RHYTON WITH KNEELING BULL, Achaemenid, VI-V c. B.C. Silver, height 8½ (21.6), maximum diameter of horn 5⅛ (13.0), depth 5 (12.7), weight 1067 grams.
Dr. Goldman, in the article cited below, notes that ". . . the formally posed bull of the rhyton is taken directly from the monumental bulls in stone that are part of the architecture at Persepolis."

Published: *7000 ans d'art en Iran*, Paris, 1961, No. 687, p. 115, pl. LXVI; Goldman, *Art Quarterly*, XXVII, 3, 1964, p. 334, fig. 11; Culican, *Medes and Persians*, 1965, pl. 56; Dorothy G. Shepherd, "Iran Between East and West," *East-West in Art*, Indiana University Press, Bloomington, Indiana, and London, 1966, No. 142, pp. 84, 93.
Exhibited: *7000 ans d'art en Iran*, Paris, 1961; *East-West in Art*, Indiana University, 1966.

1958.519

79

1957.31a & b

1957.31a & b
LION-HEAD BRACELET TERMINALS,
Achaemenid, VI-V c. B.C. Gold, height of head without clasp 1⁹⁄₃₂ (3.3), width 1⁵⁄₁₆ (3.35), depth 1¹¹⁄₁₆ (4.2), weight 52.5 grams; height of head with clasp 1³⁄₁₆ (3.0), width 1⁹⁄₃₂ (3.3), depth 1⅝ (4.5), weight 58.5 grams.
Published: Kantor, *Cincinnati Art Museum Bulletin*, Oct. 1957, pp. 15-17; Goldman, *Art Quarterly*, XXVII, 3, 1964, p. 332, fig. 7.

1957.30
BRACELET, Hamadan, Achaemenid, VI-IV c. B.C. Gold with lion-head terminals of lapis paste, diameter 4⅞ (12.4), diameter of cross-section 1¹⁄₁₆ (2.7), width of lion heads 1³⁄₁₆ (3.0), weight 330.5 grams.
Published: Kantor, *Cincinnati Art Museum Bulletin*, Oct. 1957, pp. 16-17, cover; 7000 *ans d'art en Iran*, Paris, 1961, No. 696, p. 117, pl. LXVIII; *Near Eastern Art*, Cincinnati, 1962, No. 11; Goldman, *Art Quarterly*, XXVII, 3, 1964, p. 335.
Exhibited: 7000 *ans d'art en Iran*, Paris, 1961.

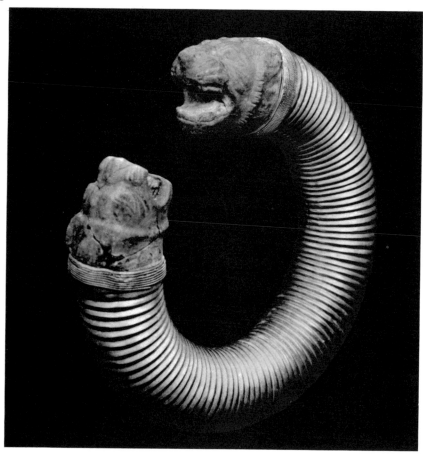

1957.30

1963.31
BOWL, Hamadan, Achaemenid, Reign of Darius
(522-485 B.C.) Gold, height 1⁹⁄₁₆ (3.9), diameter 12
(30.5), weight 1494 grams.
Inscribed: on under side of rim, cuneiform characters
for "Darius Great King" repeated in Old Persian,
Elamite and Akkadian.
Published: *7000 ans d'art en Iran*, Paris, 1961, No.
626; Ghirshman, *Ancient Iran*, 1964, fig. 310 (color);
Shine, *Museum News*, Feb. 1964, illustrated p. 34;
The Art Quarterly, XXVI, 4, 1963, p. 483; Goldman,
Art Quarterly, XXVII, 3, 1964, p. 337, fig. 12;
Cincinnati Art Museum Bulletin, VII, 3-4,
1965, illustrated.
Exhibited: *7000 ans d'art en Iran*, Paris, 1961.

1961.288

1961.288
PERSIAN GUARD, relief from Persepolis, east
face of east wing of the Council Hall, probably early
Reign of Xerxes ca. 484-482 B.C. Dark limestone,
height 24³⁄₁₆ (61.5), width 22½ (57.2).
Cf. Schmidt, *Persepolis*, I, 1953, p. 107, pl. 64-B.
Published: *Near Eastern Art, Cincinnati*, 1962, No.
12; *The Art Quarterly*, XXV, 1, 1962, p. 69; "La
chronique des arts," *Gazette des Beaux-Arts*, No.
1129, Feb. 1963, p. 66; *Cincinnati Art Museum
Bulletin*, VII, 3-4, Feb. 1965.
Gift of Mr. and Mrs. John J. Emery.

1951.133
ATTENDANT CARRYING A WINESKIN,
relief from Persepolis, probably from the south
parapet of the eastern flight of the south stairway of
the Tachari of Darius, probably early Reign of
Xerxes, ca. 484-482 B.C. Limestone, height 22⅝ (57.5)
width at base 14¾ (37.5), width at top 12 (30.5).
Cf. Schmidt, *Persepolis*, I, 1953, p. 225, pl. 133-135.
Published: Adams, "Sculpture of the Middle East,"
Cincinnati Art Museum Bulletin, I, 3, Feb. 1951, pp.
2-4; *Cincinnati Art Museum Guide*, 1956, p. 21;
Louise Bruner, "Cincinnati: A Museum With New
Walls," *Arts Magazine*, Dec. 1965, p. 37.

1951.133

1955.792

1955.792
ATTENDANT MEDE, relief from Persepolis,
probably early Reign of Xerxes ca. 484-482 B.C.
Limestone, height 9⅛ (23.2), width 9¹¹⁄₁₆ (24.6).
Exhibited: *Ancient Art in American Private Collections*, Fogg Art Museum, Harvard University,
Dec. 1954-Feb. 1955, Cat. pl. XIX, p. 21.
Gift of Mr. and Mrs. Philip R. Adams.

1963.33

1963.33

FOUNDATION PLAQUE, believed to have been found at Hamadan, Achaemenid, Reign of Artaxerxes II (405-359 B.C.) Gold, height 5⅛ (13.0), width 5⅛ (13.0), depth (0.1), weight 407.5 grams.

Inscribed: (translated by Roland Kent, *Old Persian*, p. 155 A²H_c) "A great god is Ahuramazda, the greatest of gods, who created this earth, who created yonder sky, who created man, who created happiness for man, who made Artaxerxes king, one king of many, one lord of many. Saith Artaxerxes the Great King, King of Kings, King of Countries, King in this earth, I am son of Darius the King, of Darius (who was) son of Artaxerxes the King, of Artaxerxes (who was) son of Xerxes the King, of Xerxes (who was) son of Darius the King, of Darius son of Hystaspes by name, an Achaemenian. Saith Artaxerxes the king: By the favor of Ahuramazda I am king in this great earth far and wide; Ahuramazda bestowed the kingdom upon me. Me may Ahuramazda protect, and the kingdom which he bestowed upon me, and my royal house."

One of a series of gold plaques set up by Artaxerxes; see also 1963.32.

Published: Roland G. Kent, "The Oldest Old Persian Inscriptions," *Journal of the American Oriental Society*, 66, 1946, pp. 206-212; Arthur U. Pope, "Royal Treasure of the Achaemenid Kings," *Illustrated London News*, 213, July 17, 1948, p. 58, fig. 6; *Iran*, Musée Cernuschi, Paris, 1948, No. 53; Roland G. Kent, *Old Persian*, American Oriental Series, 33, 1953, 2d Edition, A²H_c pp. 115, 155; L. Vanden Berghe, *Archéologie de l'Iran ancien*, Leiden, E. J. Brill, 1959, 1966, p. 109, pl. 135-b; "La chronique des arts," *Gazette des Beaux-Arts*, No. 1141, Feb. 1964, p. 110; *The Art Quarterly*, XXVII, 1, 1964, p. 97, illustrated p. 96; Goldman, *Art Quarterly*, XXVII, 3, 1964, p. 334; *Cincinnati Art Museum Bulletin*, VII, 3-4, Feb. 1965.

Exhibited: *Iran*, Musée Cernuschi, Paris, 1948.

Collections: Maurice Vidal, New York.

1963.32

1967.469

1963.32
FOUNDATION PLAQUE, believed to have been
found at Hamadan, Achaemenid, Reign of Artaxerxes
II (405-359 B.C.). Gold, height 3⅛ (8.0), width 5⅟₁₆
(12.8), depth (0.1), weight 266.5 grams.
Inscribed: (translated by Roland Kent, *Old Persian*,
p. 116, AsH) "Arsames, the Great King, King of Kings,
King (in) Persia, son (of) Ariaramnes the King, an
Achaemenian. Saith Arsames the King: Ahuramazda,
great God, the greatest of Gods, made me King. He
bestowed on me the land Persia, with good people,
with good horses. By the favor of Ahuramazda I hold
this land. Me may Ahuramazda protect, and my royal
house, and this land which I hold, may he protect."
One of a series of gold plaques set up by Artaxerxes II
in the names of his predecessors. Cf. 1963.33.
Published: Roland G. Kent, "The Oldest Old Persian
Inscriptions," *Journal of the American Oriental Society*, 66, 1946, pp. 206-212; Arthur U. Pope, "Royal
Treasure of the Achaemenid Kings," *Illustrated
London News*, 213, July 17, 1948, p. 58, fig. 5; *Iran*,
Musée Cernuschi, Paris, 1948, No. 54; Ronald G.
Kent, *Old Persian*, American Oriental Series, 33, 1953,
2nd Edition, AsH pp. 12, 107, 116; Schmidt, *Persepolis*,
I, 1953, p. 19, note 11; L. Vanden Berghe, *Archéologie
de l'Iran ancien*, Leiden, E. J. Brill, 1959, 1966, p. 109,
pl. 135-a; Goldman, *Art Quarterly*, XXVII, 3, 1964,
p. 334; *Cincinnati Art Museum Bulletin*, VII, 3-4,
Feb. 1965.
Exhibited: *Iran*, Musée Cernuschi, Paris, 1948.
Collections: Maurice Vidal, New York.

1967.469
EWER, said to have been found in Iran, Parthian,
I c. A.D. Bronze, height 8⅝ (21.9), width 6¼ (15.9),
depth 8⅛ (20.7), weight 2532 grams.
Published: *Cincinnati Magazine*, I, 1, Oct. 1967,
p. 20; *Pictorial Enquirer*, Cincinnati, Sept. 24, 1967,
illustrated p. 26; *The Art Quarterly*, XXX, 3-4, 1967,
p. 266, illustrated p. 271; "La chronique des arts,"
Gazette des Beaux-Arts, No. 1189, Feb. 1968, p. 137.

1952.244
TROPHY URN, Partho-Sasanian, II-IV c. A.D.
Glazed pottery, height 11 (27.8), width 5¼ (13.3),
depth 5⅛ (13.0).
Published: Dikran G. Kelekian, *The Potteries of
Persia*, Paris, 1909, fig. 1; Kelekian, *The Kelekian

Collection of Persian and Analagous Potteries, Paris,
1910, pl. 1; Friedrich Sarre, *L'art de la Perse ancienne*,
Paris, 1921, p. 147 (also German edition); Kurt Erd-
mann, "Partho-Sasanian Ceramics," *Burlington
Magazine*, LXVII, 389, Aug. 1935, pp. 71-77, pl. II,
fig. C; Richard Ettinghausen, "Parthian and Sasanian
Pottery, "*Survey of Persian Art*, 1938-39, 1966,
p. 672, pl. 185-B.
Exhibited: *Kelekian Collection*, Victoria and Albert
Museum, London.
Collections: Kelekian, New York.

1966.1091

EWER, Sasanian, IV-V c. A.D. Silver, height 16⅛ (41.0), weight 2,038 grams.

Published: Grabar, *Sasanian Silver*, 1967, No. 19, pp. 60, 61, 65, 66; B. L. Zimmerman, "The Lively Metalwork of the Sasanians," *Pictorial Enquirer*, Cincinnati, Sept. 24, 1967, cover, pp. 8-9; *Archives of Asian Art*, XXI, 1967-68, illustrated p. 77; "La chronique des arts," *Gazette des Beaux-Arts*, 1189, Feb. 1968, illustrated p. 46, No. 192.

Exhibited: *Sasanian Silver*, Michigan, 1967.

1955.71

BOWL WITH PORTRAIT MEDALLION, Sasanian, ca. 450 A.D. Silver, height 2¹⁵⁄₁₆ (7.6), diameter 9⅜ (23.7), weight 775 grams.

Published: M. S. Dimand, "A Group of Sasanian Silver Bowls," *Festschrift/Aus der Welt der Islamischen Kunst*, Berlin, 1959, pp. 11-14; *7000 ans d'art en Iran*, Paris, 1961, No. 794, p. 138; Goldman, *Art Quarterly*, XXVII, 3, 1964, p. 339, fig. 13; Prudence Oliver Harper, "Portrait of a King," *The Metropolitan Museum of Art Bulletin*, XXV, 3, Nov. 1966, illustrated p. 142, No. 14; Grabar, *Sasanian Silver*, 1967, No. 11, pp. 55-57; Maurice S. Dimand, "Some Early Sasanian Silver Vessels," *Survey of Persian Art*, XIV, 1968, p. 3024, pl. 1498.

Exhibited: *7000 ans d'art en Iran*, Paris, 1961; *Sasanian Silver*, Michigan, 1967.

Gift of Mr. and Mrs. Warner L. Atkins.

1957.387

PLATE WITH HUNTING SCENE, Sasanian, V c. A.D. Alloy of silver with copper and some gold, height 2¹⁄₁₆ (5.2), diameter 12³⁄₁₆ (30.9), weight 1,025 grams.

Published: Goldman, *Art Quarterly*, XXVII, 3, 1964, p. 336, fig. 13; Grabar, *Sasanian Silver*, 1967, No. 8; B. L. Zimmerman, "The Lively Metalwork of the Sasanians," *Pictorial Enquirer*, Cincinnati, Sept. 24, 1967, pp. 8-9, illustrated p. 11.

Exhibited: *Sasanian Silver*, Michigan, 1967.

1966.1091

1967.1283
RELIEF: AFFRONTED RAMPANT IBEXES,
Sasanian, V-VI c. A.D. Stucco, height 22¾ (57.8),
width 16½ (41.9), depth 3¼ (8.3).
Cf. similar panel in the Louvre.
Published: *Museum News*, Jan. 1969, p. 47.

1957.386
WINE DISH WITH GAZELLE MEDALLION,
Sasanian, V-VI c. A.D. Silver, height 1⅜ (3.5),
diameter 7¹¹⁄₁₆-7⅞ (19.6-20.0), maximum thickness of
relief ⁷⁄₃₂ (0.55), of rim ½ (0.1), weight 510.5 grams.
Published: Goldman, *Art Quarterly*, XXVII, 3, 1964,
p. 339, fig. 14; Grabar, *Sasanian Silver*, 1967, No. 30,
p. 68; B. L. Zimmerman, "The Lively Metalwork of
the Sasanians," *Pictorial Enquirer*, Cincinnati, Sept.
24, 1967, pp. 8-9.
Exhibited: *Sasanian Silver*, Michigan, illustrated
p. 11, 1967.

1951.132
HANDLE IN FORM OF A LEOPARD,
Sasanian, VI c. A.D. Bronze, height 9½ (24.1), width
4¹⁄₁₆ (10.3), depth 6⅝ (16.8).
The collar suggests that this may have been a
domesticated hunting cat such as a cheetah.
Published: Adams, *Cincinnati Art Museum Bulletin*,
I, 3, Feb. 1951, p. 6, illustrated p. 9.
Exhibited: *What in the World*, TV program,
University Museum, University of Pennsylvania,
Philadelphia, Oct. 10, 1954.

1951.131
WINE DISH WITH DUCK RONDELS,
Mazandaran, Sasanian, V c. A.D. Silver with some
gold leaf remaining fused to the silver in the center,
height 1¾ (4.4), diameter 11⁷⁄₁₆ (29.1), weight
1,223.5 grams.
Published: Adams, *Cincinnati Art Museum Bulletin*,
Feb. 1951, pp. 6-7; *Cincinnati Art Museum Guide*,
1956, p. 22; *Near Eastern Art*, Cincinnati, 1962, No. 13;
Grabar, *Sasanian Silver*, 1967, No. 31, p. 70, back cover;
B. L. Zimmerman, "The Lively Metalwork of the
Sasanians," *Pictorial Enquirer*, Cincinnati, Sept. 24,
1967, pp. 8-9, illustrated p. 11.
Exhibited: *Sasanian Silver*, Michigan, 1967.

1967.1283

1957.386

1951.131

1960.495

1967.1282

1960.495
RHYTON IN THE FORM OF A HORSE'S
HEAD, Sasanian, late VI c. A.D. Silver with details
gilded, height of nose to rim 10⅞ (26.6), width, ear
to ear 4⅜ (11.1), depth 4 5/16 (11.0).
Published: *The Illustrated London News*, April 2,
1960, p. 550, fig. 1; *The Art Quarterly*, XXIII, 4,
1960, p. 398; "La chronique des arts," *Gazette des
Beaux-Arts*, Feb. 1961, back page; *7000 ans d'art en
Iran*, Paris, 1961, No. 776, p. 134, pl. LXXXIV;
Cincinnati Art Museum Bulletin, VI, 1-4, July 1961,
illustrated; Ghirshman, *Parthian and Sasanian
Dynasties*, 1962, p. 221, illustrated. No. 263-a; *Near
Eastern Art*, Cincinnati, 1962, No. 14; *Artibus Asiae*,
XXV, 1962, p. 78, fig. 27; *The Chronicle of the Horse*,
Aug. 7, 1964, cover and p. 47; D. T. Rice, ed., *The
Dawn of European Civilization*, McGraw-Hill,
New York, 1965, p. 348, No. 23, illustrated p. 26;
Grabar, *Sasanian Silver*, 1967, No. 47; B. L.
Zimmerman, "The Lively Metalwork of the
Sasanians," *Pictorial Enquirer*, Cincinnati, Sept. 24,
1967, pp. 8-9, illustrated p. 11.
Exhibited: *7000 ans d'art en Iran*, Paris, 1961;
Sasanian Silver, Michigan, 1967.

1967.1282
BOTTLE, Sasanian. Silver with gilt medallions,
height 10 (25.4), diameter 5 13/16 (14.7), weight
790 grams.

1953.70
NECKLACE, Buwayhid, VIII c. A.D. Gold, length
22 (55.9), maximum thickness of center pendant
0.5 cm., of side pendant 0.4 cm., weight130 grams.
Said by Erich F. Schmidt in oral communication to
be "exactly like many I found in the well-shafts
at Rayy."
Exhibited: *Persian Exhibition*, University of
Michigan, Department of Fine Arts, Apr.-May, 1959,
No. 14.

1953.70

1966.1090

1958.518

1966.1090
PLATE WITH SEATED MONARCH,
Post-Sasanian, IX c. A.D. Silver with gilding,
diameter 13⅟₁₆ (33.2), weight 1572 grams.
Published: Grabar, *Sasanian Silver*, 1967, No. 14,
p. 58; B. L. Zimmerman, "The Lively Metalwork of
the Sasanians," *Pictorial Enquirer*, Sept. 24, 1967,
pp. 8-9, illustrated p. 11; *Archives of Asian Art*,
XII, 1967-68, illustrated p. 77; "La chronique des arts,"
Gazette des Beaux-Arts, Feb. 1968, p. 46, No. 190.
Exhibited: *Sasanian Silver*, Michigan, 1967.

1958.518
LION, probably from Sava, Seljuk Dynasty, XIII c.
A.D. Pottery with turquoise blue glaze, height 23¹³⁄₃₂
(59.4), width 9¹⁵⁄₁₆ (25.3), depth 17⅛ (43.5).
Published: Arthur U. Pope, "Ceramic Art in Islamic
Times. A History," *Survey of Persian Art*, 1938-39,
1966, p. 1631, pl. 766, 767; Phyllis Ackerman, *Guide
to the Exhibition of Persian Art*, New York, 1940,
p. 461; Pope, *Masterpieces*, 1945, p. 78, pl. 98, p. 134;
Charles K. Wilkinson, *Iranian Ceramics*, Asia House
Gallery, New York, 1963, No. 46, p. 128, pl. 46.
Exhibited: *Persian Art*, New York, 1940; *In Honor of
the Shah*, New York, 1949-50; *Iranian Ceramics*,
Asia House Gallery, New York, Oct.-Dec., 1963.
Collections: H. Kevorkian.

1952.273
INCENSE BURNER, Seljuk Dynasty, XII c. A.D.
Silver with engraved gilt and niello decoration,
height 2⅝ (6.8), diameter of waist 6½ (16.7), of
mouth 6 (15.2), weight 271 grams.
Inscribed: around outside of rim, as yet
uninterpreted.

Published: Ralph Harari, "Metalwork after the
Early Islamic Period," *Survey of Persian Art*,
1938-39, 1966, p. 2503, pl. 1354-B; *Elite 60/Metalli
islamici*, Milano, Fratelli Fabbri, 1966,
pp. 28-29, No. 9.
Exhibited: Kelekian Loan, Victoria and Albert
Museum, London, 1911-1951; *Persian Exhibition*,
Department of Fine Arts, University of Michigan,
Apr.-May 1959, No. 16.
Collections: Kelekian, New York.

1952.273

1967.1101
BOAR HUNT, region of Kubatchi, Daghestan,
Seljuk Dynasty, XII-XIII c. A.D. Stone relief, height
9¹¹⁄₁₆ (24.6), width 39⅜ (100.0).
Cf. Freer Gallery relief 36.5 and Metropolitan
Museum of Art relief 38.96.
Published: A. S. Bashkiroff, *The Art of Daghestan,*
Moscow, 1931, pl. 8; *The Dark Ages,* Worcester Art
Museum, 1937, No. 53; C. R. Morey, "Art of the
Dark Ages: A Unique Show," *The Art News,*
Feb. 20, 1937, illustrated p. 16; Alfred Salmony,
"Daghestan Sculptures," *Ars Islamica,* X, 1943,
pp. 153-163, fig. 5.
Exhibited: *Exhibition of Persian Art,* London, 1931;
The Dark Ages, Worcester Art Museum, Feb.-Mar.
1937, No. 53; *Persian Art,* New York, 1940.
Collections: Kelekian, New York.
Gift of Mr. and Mrs. John J. Emery.

India and Southeast Asia

India

1952.187
RELIEF, Amaravati, Andhra Dynasty, late II to early III c. A.D. Greenish-white marble with traces of sizing and red paint, height 20¹⁹⁄₃₂ (52.3), width 13⅝ (34.6), depth 2⅜ (6.1).
Published: Philip R. Adams, "Five Buddhist Sculptures," *Cincinnati Art Museum Bulletin*, III, 2, March 1953, pp. 3-5; *The Art Quarterly*, Autumn 1953, illustrated p. 194; *Cincinnati ArtMuseum Guide*, 1956, p. 27.
Anonymous Gift.

1952.187

1962.423
HEAD OF BUDDHA, Gandhara, II-IV c. A.D.
Stucco, height 8¼ (21.0), width 5⁵⁄₁₆ (13.5),
depth 4⅞ (12.5).
Published: *Archives of Chinese Art*, XVII, 1963, p. 58.
Collections: Kenneth de Burgh Codrington.
The William T. and Louise Taft Semple Collection.

Figures and Fragments of Architectural Decoration,
Gandhara, Swat, II-III c. A.D., gray schist:

1962.455
SEATED BUDDHA, height 26⅞ (68.3), width
14⁵⁄₃₂ (36.0), depth 6⅜ (16.2).

1962.425
SEATED BODHISATTVA, height 9¹³⁄₁₆ (24.9),
width 5¾ (14.6), depth 2⅝ (6.6).

1962.424
TWO DISCIPLES, height 8³⁄₁₆ (20.9), width 5⅝
(14.2), depth 2³⁄₁₆ (5.6).

1962.447
DECORATIVE MOLDING WITH RELIEF
OF PAIRS OF GESTICULATING FIGURES
ALTERNATING WITH COLUMNS, height
2⅞ (7.4), width 10⅛ (25.8), depth 2³⁄₃₂ (5.3).

1962.448
DECORATIVE MOLDING, relief of alternating
busts and pilasters, height 2½ (6.4), width 17⁷⁄₁₆
(44.3), depth 2³⁄₁₆ (5.5).

1962.426
DECORATIVE RELIEF, two praying figures,
a column, and a fire altar with attendant figures,
height 5⅛ (13.0), width 6⅞ (17.4), depth 1¹³⁄₁₆ (4.6).

1962.449
FRAGMENT OF CURVED REVETMENT,
decorative relief in two zones of Buddhist legend,
height 8½ (21.6), width 18⁹⁄₁₆ (47.2), depth 1¾ (4.5).

1962.439
COLUMN BASE decorated with Buddhist scenes
in relief, height 4⁷⁄₁₆ (11.2), width 7³⁄₁₆ (18.2), depth
7⅛ (18.1). Square base; cylindrical hole through
center, diameter 3½ (8.9).

1962.440
COLUMN BASE decorated with Buddhist scenes
in relief, height 4⅜ (11.1), width 7⅜ (18.7), depth
6¾ (17.1). Square base; cylindrical hole through
center, diameter 1 (2.5).
Published: *Archives of Chinese Art*, XVII, 1963, p. 58;
Cincinnati Art Museum Bulletin, VII, 3-4, Feb. 1965.
Collections: Kenneth de Burgh Codrington.
The William T. and Louise Taft Semple Collection.

1962.420
HEAD, Gandhara, III-IV c. A.D. Stucco with traces
of polychromy, height 3³⁄₁₆ (8.1), width 2⅜ (6.0),
depth 3¼ (8.2).
Published: Archives of Chinese Art, XVII, 1963, p. 58.
The William T. and Louise Taft Semple Collection.

1962.418
HEAD, Gandhara, III-IV c. A.D. Stucco, height 3¹⁵⁄₁₆
(10.0), width 3⁵⁄₁₆ (8.5), depth 3⅜ (8.6).
Published: *Archives of Chinese Art*, XVII, 1963, p. 58;
Cincinnati Art Museum Bulletin, VII, 3-4,
Feb. 1965, illustrated.
The William T. and Louise Taft Semple Collection.

1962.422
HEAD, Gandhara, III-IV c. A.D. Stucco, height 4⁵⁄₁₆
(11.0), width 3⅝ (9.2), depth 3¼ (8.3).
Published: *Archives of Chinese Art*, XVII, 1963, p. 58.
The William T. and Louise Taft Semple Collection.

1962.421
HEAD, Gandhara, III-IV c. A.D. Stucco, height 3⅞
(9.9), width 2⅞ (7.3), depth 3 (7.6).
Published: *Archives of Chinese Art*, XVII, 1963, p. 58.
The William T. and Louise Taft Semple Collection.

1962.419
HEAD OF BUDDHA, Gandhara, III-IV c. A.D.
Stucco, height 5⁵⁄₁₆ (13.5), width 3¼ (8.3),
depth 3⅛ (7.9).
Published: *Archives of Chinese Art*, XVII, 1963, p. 58.
The William T. and Louise Taft Semple Collection.

1962.455

1962.449

99

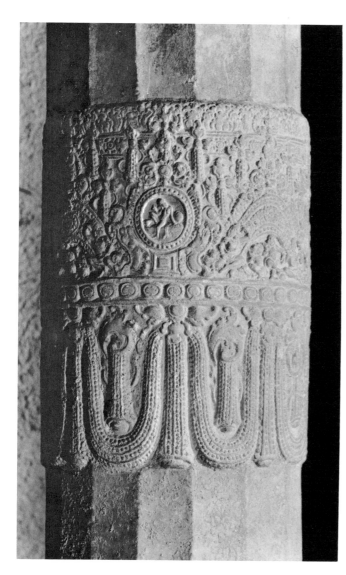

1950.75

1950.75 and 1950.76
PAIR OF COLUMNS, Amaravati region, Pallava Dynasty, early VII c. A.D. Gray-green Deccan marble, (1950.75) height 103 (261.7), diameter of capital 14¹⁵⁄₁₆ (38.0), diameter of shaft 8⅜ (21.3), width of base 11½ (29.2); (1950.76) height 103⅜ (262.5), diameter of capital 15⅜ (39.0), diameter of shaft 9⅛ (23.2), width of base 11¹³⁄₁₆ (30.0).
These columns are said to have been reworked in the VII century when the Buddhist temple of their original setting was rededicated to Siva. Another pair is in the collection of the Museum of Fine Arts in Boston, and still another is in the collection of the William Rockhill Nelson Gallery, Kansas City, Missouri.
Published: John Pope, *Exhibition of Sculpture of Greater India*, Bradford Press, N. Y., 1942, No. 25, illustrated p. 53; Adams, *Cincinnati Art Museum Bulletin*, Feb. 1951, cover, p. 9.
Exhibited: *Sculpture of Greater India*, C. T. Loo, 1942.

1962.446
HEAD OF HANUMAN, Southern Rajputana, X-XIII c. A.D. Gray sandstone with traces of white coating, height 5⅝ (14.3), width 5 (12.7), depth 5½ (14.0).
The William T. and Louise Taft Semple Collection.

1962.442
SIVA AND PARVATI/UMA-MAHESVARA, probably Western Deccan, XIV-XV c. A.D. Brass, height 6¹⁄₁₆ (15.4), width 3¹⁵⁄₁₆ (10.1), depth 2¹³⁄₁₆ (7.1).
Small votive group, Siva seated with Parvati on his knee, the Bull Nanda under their feet, Ganesha on the Rat to his left.
The William T. and Louise Taft Semple Collection.

1962.450
ATTENDANT FIGURE WITH CAURI, Rajputana, XV-XVI c. A.D. White marble, height 17½ (44.5), width 6½ (16.5), depth 3¾ (9.5).
Published: *Archives of Chinese Art*, XVII, 1963, p. 58; *Cincinnati Art Museum Bulletin*, VII, 3-4, Feb. 1965.
The William T. and Louise Taft Semple Collection.

1950.76

1940.1079
SIVA NATARAJA, region of Madras, XVI-XVII c.
A.D. Bronze, height 33¹³⁄₁₆ (85.9), width 23¼ (59.0),
depth 12 (30.5).
Exhibited: *Masterworks of Sculpture,* John Herron
Art Institute, Indianapolis, 1956.
Gift of George Warrington in memory of Elsie
Holmes Warrington.

1940.1079

1962.459

1962.459
JAIN SHRINE, Gujerat (Patam), XVII c. A.D.
Wood, height 85⅜ (216.9), width 66⅛ (168.0),
depth 33¼ (84.4).
The shrine comprises a wall with a niche in it and a
heavy projecting roof supported by two columns, all
elaborately carved, painted and gilded, with figures,
animals and decorative forms.
Published: *Archives of Chinese Art*, XVII, 1963, p. 45,
fig. 7; *Cincinnati Art Museum Bulletin*, VII, 3-4,
Feb. 1965.
The William T. and Louise Taft Semple Collection.

1962.433
SEATED TIRTHANKARA, Jaipur, XVIII-XIX,
c. A.D. Red stone, height 9³⁄₁₆ (23.3), width 7⅝ (19.4),
depth 3⁹⁄₁₆ (9.0).
The William T. and Louise Taft Semple Collection.

1962.432
TIRUJNANA SAMBHANDAR, South India,
XIX c. A.D. Bronze, height 8¹⁄₁₆ (20.5), width 4⅜ (11.1),
depth 3 (7.7).
The William T. and Louise Taft Semple Collection.

1962.452
PEACOCK, XIX c. A.D. Bronze, height 7¼ (18.4),
width 2⅞ (7.2), depth 4⅞ (12.3).
The body of the bird, which is hollow, is decorated
with engraved feather motif. The tail was a
separate piece bolted on; but is now missing.
The William T. and Louise Taft Semple Collection.

1962.431
MAHOUT, XIX, c. A.D. Bronze, height 7³⁄₁₆ (18.2),
width 4¾ (12.1), depth 4⁹⁄₁₆ (11.6).
Seated figure, right leg doubled back, left leg hanging
down, left hand raised to hold prod (missing),
right hand on knee.
Published: *Cincinnati Art Museum Bulletin*, VII, 3-4,
Feb. 1965, illustrated.
Exhibited: *Master Bronzes Selected from Museums
and Collections in America*, Albright Art Gallery,
Buffalo, N.Y., Feb. 1937, No. 108.
The William T. and Louise Taft Semple Collection.

1962.443
HANUMAN, XIX c, A.D. Bronze, height 8 (20.3),
width 2¾ (7.0), depth 3¹⁄₁₆ (7.8).

Standing figure, hands before him, with palms
pressed together.
Published: *Cicinnati Art Museum Bulletin*, VII, 3-4,
Feb. 1965, illustrated.
The William T. and Louise Taft Semple Collection.

Cambodia

1946.6
HEAD OF A DHYANI BUDDHA, Khmer
period, X-XI c. A.D. Reddish sandstone with traces of
paint, height 21²¹⁄₃₂ (55.0), width 16¾ (42.5),
depth 8⁵⁄₁₆ (21.1).
Published: Philip R. Adams, "Sculpture of the Far
East," *Cincinnati Art Museum Bulletin*, I, 5-6,
1951, p. 4.

1962.456
FEMALE BUST, ca. XIII c. A.D. Gray sandstone,
height 18⁵⁄₃₂ (46.1), width 14¹¹⁄₃₂ (36.4), depth 6⁵⁄₃₂ (25.5).
The original setting evidently was the side wall of a
niche. Since the figure could be seen only in profile
arbitrary distortions, similar to those to be seen on
pediments of the Parthenon were introduced to
give a greater impression of solidity.
The William T. and Louise Taft Semple Collection.

1952.113

Java

1952.113
HEAD OF A DHYANI BUDDHA, Borobudur,
VIII-IX c. A.D. Gray stone, height 13⅛ (33.3), width
9%₃₂ (23.6), depth 9%₃₂ (23.6).
Published: John Pope, *Exhibition of Sculpture of
Greater India*, Bradford Press, N. Y., 1942, No. 50,
p. 38, illustrated p. 65; Adams, *Cincinnati Art
Museum Bulletin*, Mar. 1953, pp. 6-7.
Exhibited: *Sculpture of Greater India*, C. T. Loo,
N. Y., 1942, No. 50.
Collections: C. T. Loo, New York.

Nepal

1962.427
STANDING BUDDHA, X-XI c. A.D. Gilt bronze,
height 6¾ (17.2), width 2¾ (7.0), depth 1⅜ (3.5).
Published: *Archives of Chinese Art*, XVII, 1963, p. 58;
Cincinnati Art Museum Bulletin, VII, 3-4, Feb.
1965, illustrated.
The William T. and Louise Taft Semple Collection.

1962.428
SEATED BUDDHA, X-XII c. A.D. Gilt bronze,
height 4¾ (12.0), width 3⅞ (9.8), depth 2⁷⁄₁₆ (6.2).
The William T. and Louise Taft Semple Collection.

1962.445
AVALOKITESVARA, XIV c. A.D. Bronze, height
24¾ (62.9), width 6⅞ (17.4), depth 4¼ (10.8).
Published: *Archives of Chinese Art*, XVII, 1963, p. 58;
Stella Kramrisch, *The Art of Nepal*, The Asia Society,
New York, 1964, No. 19, p. 132; *Cincinnati Art
Museum Bulletin*, VII, 3-4, Feb. 1965, illustrated.
Exhibited: *The Art of Nepal*, The Asia Society,
1964, see above.
Collections: Mary Dodsworth.
The William T. and Louise Taft Semple Collection.

1962.445

1962.444
BUDDHA SEATED ON THE SERPENT'S
COILS AND SHIELDED BY ITS HEADS,
XVII c. A.D. Rock crystal, height 5⅛ (13.0), width
2⅜ (6.0), depth 1²¹⁄₃₂ (4.2), weight 277 grams.
Published: Stella Kramrisch, *The Art of Nepal*, The
Asia Society, New York, 1964, No. 63, p. 141
and illustrated.
Exhibited: *The Art of Nepal*, The Asia Society, 1964.
The William T. and Louise Taft Semple Collection.

1938.10597
BODHISATTVA, XIX c. A.D. Bronze, height 8⅛
(20.7), width 3¹⁄₁₆ (7.8), depth 2⅛ (5.4).
Gift of Mr. and Mrs. Julius Fleischmann.

1962.441
STANDING BODHISATTVA
SURROUNDED BY AN AUREOLE, XIX-XX
c. A.D. Bronze, height 6⁹⁄₁₆ (16.6), width 3¹⁵⁄₁₆ (10.0),
depth 1²⁷⁄₃₂ (4.7).
The William T. and Louise Taft Semple Collection.

Siam

1938.10596
HEAD OF BUDDHA, XIV-XV c. A.D. Bronze,
height 3¾ (9.6), width 2¹⁄₁₆ (5.2), depth 2⅛ (5.4).
Gift of Mr. and Mrs. Julius Fleischmann.

1938.10595
HEAD OF BUDDHA, XVI c. A.D. Bronze, height
4⅝ (11.7), width 2¼ (5.6), depth 2½ (6.4).
Gift of Mr. and Mrs. Julius Fleischmann.

1938.10593
HEAD OF BUDDHA, XVIII c. A.D. Bronze,
height 4½ (11.5), width 2⅜ (6.0), depth 2⁹⁄₁₆ (6.5).
Gift of Mr. and Mrs. Julius Fleischmann.

1938.10600
SEATED BUDDHA, XVIII c. A.D. Gilt bronze,
height 12⅝ (32.0), width 6¼ (15.9), depth 5 (12.7).
Gift of Mr. and Mrs. Julius Fleischmann.

China

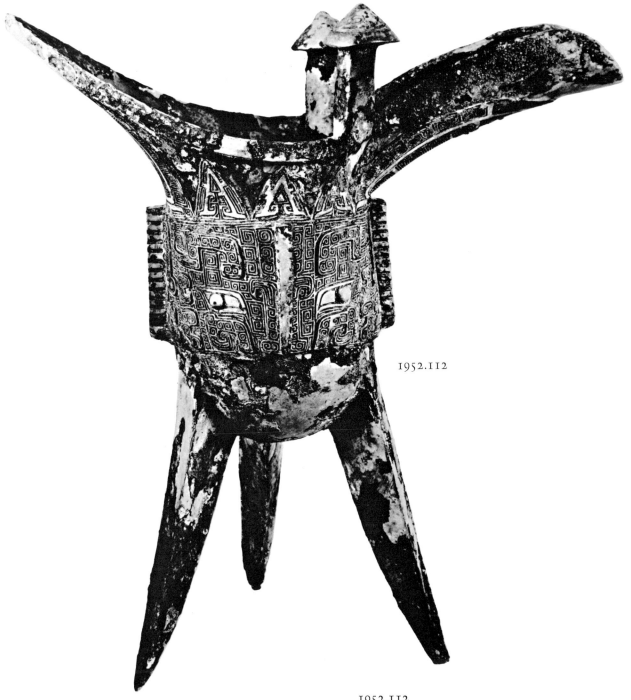

1952.112

1952.112
CHUEH (libation cup), Shang Dynasty, 1766-1122
B.C. Bronze, height 8¹³⁄₁₆ (22.4), width 7¹⁵⁄₁₆ (20.1),
depth 4¼ (10.9), weight 1202 grams.
Published: *Archives of Chinese Art*, IX, 1955,
illustrated p. 80.

1948.74
CHIA (tripod ceremonial vessel), Shang Dynasty,
1766-1122 B.C. Bronze, height 11 (28.0), width at posts
6¹⁵⁄₁₆ (17.6), diameter of vessel 6⁷⁄₁₆ (16.3), width of
vessel plus handle 7⁵⁄₁₆ (18.5), weight 2462.5 grams.
Inscribed: Single character inside bowl.
Published: *Cincinnati Art Museum Guide,*
1956, p. 33.
Given in honor of Mr. and Mrs. Charles F.
Williams by their children.

1948.75
I (rectangular ceremonial vessel), Shang Dynasty,
1766-1122 B.C. Bronze, height of vessel 7⅛ (18.0),
of lid 5 (12.7), both together 11⅜ (29.0), width lid
7½ (19.1), vessel 7⁷⁄₁₆ (18.8), depth lid 6⁷⁄₁₆ (16.4),
vessel 6½ (16.7), weight of lid 1901 grams, of vessel
4811 grams.
Inscribed: single impressed character inside lid and
inside bottom of vessel.
Published: "Cincinnati Art Museum News,"
Magazine of Art, II, 8, Dec. 1947, p. i; Max Loehr,
"The Bronze Styles of the Anyang Period," *Archives
of Chinese Art,* VII, 1953, p. 42, fig. 18; William
Charles White, *Bronze Sculpture of Ancient China,*
Royal Ontario Museum of Archaeology, Museum
Studies No. V, Toronto, 1956, p. 52; Max Loehr, *Ritual
Vessels of Bronze Age China,* The Asia Society, New
York, 1968, No. 38, pp. 58, 90, 92, 93, 128, 177, 183.
Exhibited: *Ritual Vessels of Bronze Age China,* Asia
House, N.Y., 1968, No. 38.
Given in honor of Mr. and Mrs. Charles F.
Williams by their children.

1948.74

1948.75

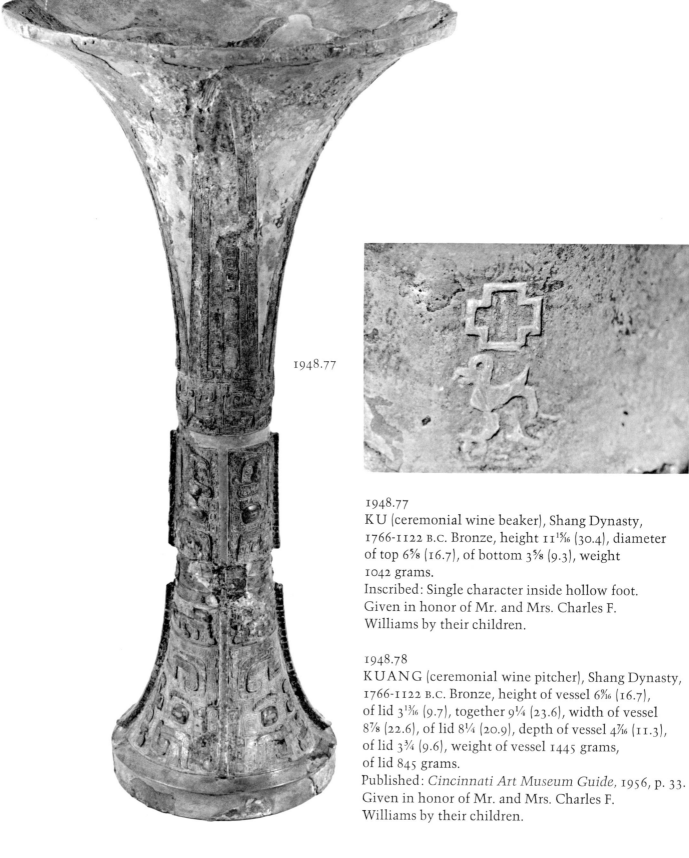

1948.77

1948.77
KU (ceremonial wine beaker), Shang Dynasty,
1766-1122 B.C. Bronze, height 11¹⁵⁄₁₆ (30.4), diameter
of top 6⅝ (16.7), of bottom 3⅝ (9.3), weight
1042 grams.
Inscribed: Single character inside hollow foot.
Given in honor of Mr. and Mrs. Charles F.
Williams by their children.

1948.78
KUANG (ceremonial wine pitcher), Shang Dynasty,
1766-1122 B.C. Bronze, height of vessel 6⁹⁄₁₆ (16.7),
of lid 3¹³⁄₁₆ (9.7), together 9¼ (23.6), width of vessel
8⅞ (22.6), of lid 8¼ (20.9), depth of vessel 4⁷⁄₁₆ (11.3),
of lid 3¾ (9.6), weight of vessel 1445 grams,
of lid 845 grams.
Published: *Cincinnati Art Museum Guide*, 1956, p. 33.
Given in honor of Mr. and Mrs. Charles F.
Williams by their children.

1948.78

1948.76

1948.73

1948.73
YU (ceremonial vessel), early Chou Dynasty,
1122-255 B.C. Bronze, height of lid 2½ (6.4), width of
lid 7⅝ (16.9), depth of lid 4⅛ (10.4), height of vessel
5⅞ (13.8), width of vessel 6½ (16.5), depth of vessel
4¹⁵⁄₁₆ (12.6), height together 7⁷⁄₁₆ (18.9), weight of vessel
1530.5 grams, weight of vessel and lid 2007.5 grams.
Inscribed: Two characters inside vessel at
center of base.
Published: Phyllis Ackerman, *Ritual Bronzes of
China*, Dryden Press, New York, 1945, pl. 4,
text pp. 81, 88, 99, 104.
Given in honor of Mr. and Mrs. Charles F.
Williams by their children.

1948.76
CHUNG (bell), late Chou Dynasty, 1122-255 B.C.
Bronze, height 16¹¹⁄₁₆ (42.4), width 8⅝ (22.0), depth
11¼ (28.5), weight 16,618.5 grams.
Exhibited: *Masterpieces of Chinese Art*, Virginia
Museum of Fine Arts, Richmond, Nov. 19-Jan. 2,
1954-55.
Given in honor of Mr. and Mrs. Charles F.
Williams by their children.

1950.74

1950.74
TOMB RELIEF, Han Dynasty, style of Wu
Liang-Tzu, 206 B.C.-220 A.D. Stone, height 17⅞ (45.4),
width of top 65 (165.1), of bottom 59½ (151.1).
This slab has been sawn from a thicker ceiling beam
in its original setting.
Published: *An Exhibition of Chinese Stone Sculpture,*
C. T. Loo, Inc., text by C. T. Loo and Alfred Salmony,
Wm. Bradford Press, New York, 1940, No. 5,
illustrated pl. III; Adams, *Cincinnati Art Museum
Bulletin,* Summer 1951, cover, p. 6; *Cincinnati Art
Museum Bulletin,* II, 1, Nov. 1951, illustrated p. 2.
Exhibited: C. T. Loo, Inc., 1940, see above.
Collections: C. T. Loo, New York.

1949.146
WILD ASS, Ordos Region, Han Dynasty, 206
B.C.-220 A.D. Bronze, height 3⅛ (7.8), width ¾ (0.8),
depth 3 (7.6).
Exhibited: *Carnival of Animals,* Columbus Gallery
of Fine Arts, Dec. 1950; University Museum TV
Program, *What in the World?,* University of
Pennsylvania, Philadelphia, Oct. 10, 1954.
Gift of John J. Emery.

1962.454
HEAD OF A BODHISATTVA, from Lung Men
cave, Wei Dynasty, 221-618 A.D., ca. V c. Gray
limestone, height 11 (27.9), width 5⅛ (13.0), depth
4¹³⁄₁₆ (12.3).
Published: *Archives of Chinese Art,* XVII, 1963, fig. 6,
p. 44; *Cincinnati Art Museum Bulletin,* VII, 3-4,
Feb. 1965, illustrated.
The William T. and Louise Taft Semple Collection.

1962.451

1946.11

1962.451
SEATED MAITREYA, from Lung Men cave
temple in Shansi Province, Wei Dynasty, V c. A.D.
Painted stone, height 14 (35.6), width 6⁹⁄₁₆ (15.7).
Published: *Archives of Chinese Art*, XVII, 1963, p. 58;
Cincinnati Art Museum Bulletin, VII, 3-4,
Feb. 1965, illustrated.
The William T. and Louise Taft Semple Collection.

1946.11
VOTIVE STELA WITH BUDDHIST
TRINITY, Wei Dynasty, 522 A.D. Dark limestone,
height 79½ (202.0), width 39⁹⁄₁₆ (100.5).
Inscribed: A dedicatory text on the back of the

stela has not yet been fully read, but in addition to
giving the date suggests that the stela memorialized
a flood-control project whose donors are depicted
with their ceremonial umbrellas.
Published: Martha Davidson, "Great Chinese
Sculptures in America," *Art News Annual*, 1939,
p. 74, figs. 10-13; *An Exhibition of Chinese Stone
Sculpture*, C. T. Loo, Inc., text by C. T. Loo and
Alfred Salmony, Wm. Bradford Press, New York,
1940, No. 16 and pl. IX, X, XI; Adams, *Cincinnati Art
Museum Bulletin*, Summer 1951, pp. 6-10; *Cincinnati
Art Museum Bulletin*, II, 1, Nov. 1951, illustrated p. 2;
Cincinnati Art Museum Guide, 1956, p. 35.
Exhibited: C. T. Loo, Inc., 1940, see above.
Collections: C. T. Loo, New York.

1962.429
SEATED BUDDHA, Wei Dynasty, V-VI c. A.D.
Gilt bronze, height 8¹⁵⁄₁₆ (22.7), width 4⅜ (11.1),
depth 2¹¹⁄₁₆ (6.7), weight 930 grams.
Dated 580 by inscription on back.
Mr. Munsterberg believes this piece was made
earlier than the date inscribed on the back, perhaps
around 480.
Published: Hugo Munsterberg, *Chinese Buddhist
Bronzes*, Tuttle, Rutland, Vermont, and Tokyo,
1967, p. 27, figs. 7-a, 7-b, p. 40.
The William T. and Louise Taft Semple Collection.

1962.430
DOG OR HYENA, Wei Dynasty, ca. VI c. A.D.
Gilt bronze, height 5⁷⁄₁₆ (13.8), width 3½ (9.0),
depth 6¹³⁄₁₆ (17.6).
Published: *Archives of Chinese Art*, XVII, 1963, p. 58;
Cincinnati Art Museum Bulletin, VII, 3-4,
Feb. 1965, illustrated.
The William T. and Louise Taft Semple Collection.

1958.549
STELA WITH SEATED BUDDHA, Honan,
Northern Wei Dynasty, 521 A.D. Stone, height 9⅞
(25.0), width of front 7¼ (18.4), of back 7⁹⁄₃₂ (18.6),
depth 2⅝ (6.7).
Dated by inscription on base.
Published: *An Exhibition of Chinese Stone
Sculpture*, C. T. Loo, Inc., text by C. T. Loo and
Alfred Salmony, Wm. Bradford Press, New York,
1940, No. 11, illustrated pl. VII; *Archives of Chinese
Art*, XIII, 1959, illustrated p. 90, fig. 7.
Exhibited: C. T. Loo, Inc., 1940, see above.
Collections: C. T. Loo, New York.
Gift of Mr. and Mrs. Philip R. Adams.

1952.110
TA SHIH-SHIH, Northern Honan, Northern
Ch'i Dynasty, 565-575 A.D. Marble with traces of
polychromy, height 69 (175.3), width 20⅝ (52.3),
depth 20¾ (52.6).
Sirén (see below) sees this figure and its companion
figure of Kwanyin (1952.111) as flanking figures
for a Buddha that is dated by inscription, 575 A.D.
Published: Osvald Sirén, "Marble Sculptures of the
Transition Period," *Bulletin*, No. 12, Museum of Far
Eastern Antiquities, Stockholm, 1940, pp. 474-478,

pl. I-b; Adams, *Cincinnati Art Museum Bulletin*,
March 1953, pp. 5-7; *Art Digest*, Aug. 1953, p. 13,
illustrated; *Archives of Chinese Art*, VII, 1953, p. 84,
fig. 6 (upper right).
Exhibited: *Chinese Sculpture*, Columbus Gallery of
Fine Arts, Feb. 1943.

1962.429

1950.72

1952.111

KWANYIN, Northern Honan, Northern Ch'i
Dynasty, 565-575 A.D. Marble with traces of
polychromy, height 68⁷⁄₁₆ (173.9), width 20¼ (51.4),
depth 20½ (52.0).

Sirén (see below) sees this figure and its companion
figure of Ta Shih-Shih (1952.110) as flanking figures
for a Buddha that is dated by inscription, 575 A.D.

Published: Osvald Sirén, "Marble Sculptures of the
Transition Period," *Bulletin*, No. 12, Museum of Far
Eastern Antiquities, Stockholm, 1940, pp. 474-478,
pl. I-c; *An Exhibition of Chinese Stone Sculpture*,
C. T. Loo, Inc., text by C. T. Loo and Alfred
Salmony, Wm. Bradford Press, New York, 1940,
No. 25, pl. XVIII; *Cincinnati Art Museum Bulletin*.
II, 1, Nov. 1951, illustrated, p. 3; Adams, *Cincinnati
Art Museum Bulletin*, March 1953, pp. 5-7; *Art
Digest*, August 1953, p. 13 (not illustrated); *Archives
of Chinese Art*, VII, 1953, p. 84, fig. 6 (lower left);
Cincinnati Art Museum Guide, 1956, p. 31.

Exhibited: C. T. Loo, Inc., 1940, see above; *Chinese
Sculpture*, Columbus Gallery of Fine Arts, Feb. 1943.

Collections: C. T. Loo, New York.

1950.72

BODHISATTVA, Sui Dynasty, 598-618 A.D.
Limestone, height 32½ (76.4), width 12⅞ (32.7),
depth 5⅛ (13.0).

A companion piece to this bodhisattva, somewhat
less damaged, is in the collection of the Freer
Gallery of Art, Washington, D.C.

Published: Osvald Sirén, *Chinese Sculpture*, London,
1925, I, p. 83, No. 308, III, pl. 308; Adams, *Cincinnati
Art Museum Bulletin*, Summer 1951, pp. 10-13;
Cincinnati Art Museum Guide, 1956, p. 32.

Collections: Belle da Costa Greene, New York.

1952.111

1952.109
HAND OF BUDDHA, Lung Men caves, T'ang
Dynasty, 618-907 A.D. Limestone with polychromy,
height 23⁷⁄₁₆ (59.9), width 8¾ (22.2), depth 8¹⁄₁₆ (20.4).
Published: Adams, *Cincinnati Art Museum Bulletin*,
March 1953, pp. 2, 6; *T'ang*, Los Angeles County
Museum, 1957, No. 45, illustrated.
Exhibited: *T'ang*, Los Angeles County Museum,
Jan. 8-Feb. 17, 1957.

1962.453
FEMALE HEAD, T'ang Dynasty, IX c. A.D. Cast
iron, height 11⁵⁄₁₆ (28.7), width 6¼ (15.9),
depth 6⅝ (16.8).
The William T. and Louise Taft Semple Collection.

1950.73
KWANYIN, Sung Dynasty, 960-1279 A.D. Painted
wood, height 38³¹⁄₃₂ (99.0), width at base 32⅛ (79.1),
depth 21⅞ (55.5).
Published: Adams, *Cincinnati Art Museum Bulletin*,
Summer 1951, p. 17; *Cincinnati Art Museum
Bulletin*, II, 1, Nov. 1951, illustrated p. 3; *Record
of the Art Museum, Princeton University*, XII,
1953, No. 1, p. 33, fig. 22.
Collections: C. T. Loo, New York.

1950.73

1948.202, .203
PAIR OF HORSES, Ch'ing Dynasty, late XVIII c.
Jade, (1948.202) height 10¼ (26.0), width 3¼ (8.2),
depth 12⁹⁄₁₆ (32.0); (1948.203) height 10¹⁄₁₆ (25.5),
width 3³⁄₁₆ (8.1), depth 12⅞ (32.6).
The jade was probably mined as early as the Ming
Dynasty and not worked until later.
Gift of the Marquis and Marquise de
Talleyrand-Perigord.

1962.436
WOMAN WITH A PHOENIX, ca. 1920-1930.
Dark green jade, height 9⅝ (24.4), width 3⅞ (9.8),
depth 2⁵⁄₁₆ (5.9).
The William T. and Louise Taft Semple Collection.

1962.434
PHOENIX, ca. 1920-1930. Dark green jade, height
10¼ (26.1), width 2¹⁄₁₆ (5.2), depth 3¹⁵⁄₁₆ (10.0).
The William T. and Louise Taft Semple Collection.

1962.435
PHOENIX, ca. 1920-1930. Dark green jade, height
10³⁄₁₆ (25.9), width 1⅞ (4.8), depth 4 (10.1).
The William T. and Louise Taft Semple Collection.

Medieval and Renaissance Europe

1946.8

France

1946.8
VIRGIN, region of Toulouse, Romanesque, ca.
1130 A.D. Wood with polychromy, height 34 (86.4),
width 11⅛ (28.3), depth 13⅜ (34.0).
The head was carved from a separate block of wood
as were the missing hands holding the child. A
removable panel was set in the back of the hollow
figure, suggesting its original purpose as a reliquary,
or processional figure. The color is largely original.
Published: *Cincinnati Art Museum Guide*, 1956, p. 14.

1958.548

1958.548
HEAD, St. Gilles du Gard, Provence, ca 1160 A.D.
Limestone, height 7²⁵⁄₃₂ (19.8), width 5⁹⁄₁₆ (14.1),
depth 5³⁄₃₂ (13.0).
This and two other heads of saints, most probably
came from the tympanum of a vanished north
portal. The surviving half of the tympanum is in the
St. Gilles du Gard (Gard) Musée Archéologique
at St. Gilles.
Published: *The Art Quarterly*, XXII, 3, 1959, p. 273,
illustrated p. 275; *The Renaissance of the Twelfth
Century*, Museum of Art, Rhode Island School of
Design, Providence, R. I., 1969, No. 43, pp. 122,
124-126.
Exhibited: *A Medieval Treasury*, Andrew Dickson
White Museum of Art, Cornell University, Oct.
8-Nov. 3, 1968, Munson-Williams-Proctor Institute,
Utica, Nov. 10-Dec. 8, 1968, No. 55 and p. 139; *The
Renaissance of the Twelfth Century*, Providence,
May-June, 1969, No. 43.
Gift of Mr. and Mrs. Philip R. Adams.

1952.15
GARGOYLE, Poitiers, late XII c. Limestone, height
17¹⁄₁₆ (43.3), width 28.0 (71.1), depth 15¹⁵⁄₁₆ (40.5).
Published: *Cincinnati Art Museum Bulletin*, II, No.
2, May 1952, illustrated p. 10; *Cincinnati Art
Museum Guide*, 1956, p. 12.

1966.1092
FRAGMENT OF A GARGOYLE IN THE
FORM OF A HUMAN HEAD, Paris, late XII-
early XIV c. Limestone, height 8 (20.3), width 10⅝
(27.0), depth 10 (25.4).
The stone is the *pierre de meulier* of the Ile de la
Cité in Paris. The fragment is said to have been
found beneath the *chantier* or workshop of Nôtre
Dame and may well be one of the innumerable
damaged sculptures removed by Viollet-le-Duc's
restoration begun in 1845.
Gift of Carl Strauss, John Strauss and Mary Sacknoff
in honor of their mother Mrs. Albert I. Strauss.

1952.13
CAPITAL, Provence, XII c. Limestone, height 9⁷⁄₁₆
(24.0), width 9⅞ (25.1), depth 10 (25.5).
Exhibited: Television program, *What in the World?*
The University Museum, University of Pennsylvania,
Philadelphia, 1960

1952.15

1952.14
CAPITAL, region of Toulouse, XII c. Limestone,
height 11⅜ (28.8), width 15⅜ (39.1), depth 10⁹⁄₁₆ (26.8).

1946.7
DONOR OF THE HOSPICE OF SALINS,
Gothic, 1260-1305. Limestone, height 69¾ (177.2),
width 21⅝ (55.0), depth 14³⁄₁₆ (36.1).
The sculptor of this figure may have worked on the
west facade of Rheims Cathedral about 1260-1280.
There are also similarities to sculptures on the
Cathedral of Strasbourg. Four evangelists are said
to have been listed in a catalog of the antiquities of
Salins about 1908, of which one is in private
possession and two have disappeared. Since then, and
probably before, this figure of St. John has been
known as a portrait of the donor of the hospice.
Published: "Art at the Fair," *Art News Supplement*,
1940, illustrated p. 68; "Cincinnati Art Museum
News," *Magazine of Art*, Dec. 1946, p. ii; *Cincinnati
Art Museum Guide*, 1956, p. 13; "Sculpture, History
of," *American Oxford Encyclopedia*, Vol. XII,
The Arts, p. 474 (1963); José Pijoan, *Summa Artis,
Historia General del Arte*, Espasa-Calpe, S.A.,
Madrid, 1947, XI, p. 228, fig. 387.
Exhibited: Loan Exhibition of French Gothic Art,
Detroit Institute of Arts, Nov. 16-Dec. 6, 1928, No.
25; New York World's Fair, 1939.
Collections: Larcade, Versailles, Kelekian, New York.

1946.7

1948.164

1952.21

1952.16
MAN WITH DRAGON, Angers, XIII c.
Limestone, height 15⁵⁄₃₂ (38.5), width 15¼ (38.7),
depth 9¼ (23.5).

1952.17
CAPITAL, Ile de France, XIII c. Limestone, height
8¹¹⁄₁₆ (22.1), width 8⅜ (21.2), depth 8⅛ (20.7).

1952.18
CAPITAL, Champagne, region of Rheims, XIII c.
Limestone, height 10⁷⁄₁₆ (26.6), width 12⅛ (30.8),
depth 10⅛ (25.7).

1952.19
CAPITAL, Ile de France, XIV, c. Limestone, height
14¼ (36.2), width 15⅛ (38.4), depth 15¼ (38.6).

1952.20
CAPITAL, region of Rheims, XIV c. Limestone,
height 11⅛ (28.3), width 9 (22.9), depth 9⅝ (24.4).

1952.22
CAPITAL, region of Bourges, XV c. Limestone,
height 10⅜ (26.3), width 17³⁄₁₆ (43.6), depth 15⅝ (39.6).

1948.164
HEAD OF AN ANGEL, Rheims, late XIII c.
Limestone with polychromy, height 9½ (24.1), width
8⅜ (21.3), depth 7⅜ (18.7).
Published: *Cincinnati Art Museum Guide*, 1956, p. 13.
Exhibited: *Masterpieces of Sculpture*, John Herron
Art Institute, Indianapolis, Ind., Feb. 8-Mar. 18, 1956.
Gift of Dikran G. Kelekian.

1952.21
VIRGIN AND CHILD, Ile de France, early XIV c.
Limestone, height 48⁵⁄₃₂ (122.3), width 16⁷⁄₃₂ (41.2),
depth 9⁹⁄₁₆ (24.3).
Published: "Cincinnati Art Museum News,"
Magazine of Art, Dec. 1947, illustrated p. ii;
Cincinnati Magazine, I, 3, Dec. 1967, illustrated p. 45.

1952.23
ST. JOHN THE BAPTIST, Burgundy, XV c.
Limestone with polychromy, height 41⁹⁄₁₆ (105.6),
width 14 (35.5), depth 10⅝ (27.0).

1952.23

Italy

1953.151
MADONNA AND CHILD, Siena, 1370-1380.
Wood with polychromy, height 62½ (158.8), width
19¹³⁄₁₆ (50.3), depth 16¼ (41.3).
Published: Enzo Carli, *La Scultura Lignea Senese*,
Electa Editrice, Milano-Firenze, 1951, footnote
pp. 36-37; *The Art Quarterly*, XVII, 2, 1954, p. 180,
Winter 1954, p. 437, illustrated p. 424; *Cincinnati
Art Museum Guide*, 1956, p. 16; *Cincinnati
Magazine*, Dec. 1967, cover.
Collections: Bardini, Florence; Hohenzollern-
Sigmaringen.

1946.4
MINO DA FIESOLE (1430/31-1484), MADONNA
AND CHILD, Florentine. Terra-cotta, height 49³⁄₁₆
(124.5), width 25¹¹⁄₁₆ (65.2).
Working model for centerpiece of Cardinal Pietro
Riario Tomb, SS Apostoli, Rome. The tomb figure
follows the model exactly. The other sculptures of
the Riario Tomb were the work of Andrea
Bregno (1421-1506).
Published: "Cincinnati Art Museum News,"
Magazine of Art, I, No. 3, Dec. 1946, p. i.
Exhibited: *Masterpieces of Sculpture*, Minneapolis
Institute of Arts, Nov. 1-Dec. 15, 1949.

1949.142
ANDREA DELLA ROBBIA (1435-1525?),
MADONNA AND CHILD, Florentine. Glazed terra-cotta,
diameter 25³⁄₁₆ (64.0).
Exhibited: *The Christmas Story*, Fort Wayne Art
School and Museum, Indiana, Nov. 29-Dec. 31, 1953.
Gift of the Marquis and Marquise de
Talleyrand-Perigord.

1953.151

1946.4

1955.746

1955.746
SCHOOL OF LEONARDO DA VINCI,
Lombardy, early XVI c., ANATOMICAL HORSE. Bronze,
height 9¹⁄₁₆ (23.0), width 2¹⁵⁄₁₆ (7.5), depth 8¾ (22.2).
Cf. Carlo Ruini, *Anatomia del cavallo, infermita, et
suoi remedi, opera nuova*, Bologna, 1598, Venice
1599, 1707 (Lorenso Baseges, ed.), illustration of
"stripped" horse appears to be drawn from
this bronze.
Published: Wilhelm Suida, "A Bronze Horse
attributed to Leonardo," *International Studio*, June
1931, pp. 15-17, 72; *Cincinnati Art Museum Guide*,
1956, pp. 15, 17; *The Art Quarterly*, XIX, 3, 1956,
p. 306; *The Chronicle of the Horse*, Berryville, Va.,
Apr. 1963, cover and p. 47.
Exhibited: *Mostra di Leonardo da Vinci*, Milan,
May-Oct. 1939, Sala della scultura, No. 13; Los
Angeles County Museum, 1949; Virginia Museum
of Fine Arts, 1952; *Italian Renaissance*, Vancouver
Art Gallery, Nov.-Dec. 1953, No. 9; Corning Glass
Center, 1953; Cooper Union, New York, Apr. 15-20,
1953; Wisconsin Union, University of Wisconsin,
Jan.-Feb. 1954.
Collections: Piero Tozzi, New York; Parrish-Watson,
New York; Prince Filangeri di Candida, Naples.

Spain

1958.93
TOMB EFFIGY OF DON SANCHO SAIZ
CARILLO, Ermita de San Andres, Mahamud,
Province of Burgos, 1250-1275. Wood with polychromy, length 92 (234.0), width 23 (58.5), depth
14½ (36.8).
Panel paintings of mourners from both sides of the
large sacrophagus, suitable for a double burial, with
castles of Castile at the ends are now in the collection
of the Museum of Catalan Art, Barcelona. They are
among the most distinguished examples of Castilian
Gothic painting.
Published: *Fortune*, Dec. 1958, p. 106, illustrated;
The Art Quarterly, XXI, 4, 1958, p. 429, illustrated
p. 428; "La chronique des arts," *Gazette des Beaux-
Arts*, Paris, Jan. 1960, p. 29, No. 101, illustrated;
Pantheon, Munich 1960, illustrated p. LXVI;
Cincinnati Art Museum Bulletin, VI, 1-4, July 1961,
illustrated; Philip R. Adams, "Tomb Effigy of Don
Sancho Saiz Carillo," *Cincinnati Art Museum
Bulletin*, VII, 2, Mar. 1963, pp. 13-17; *Emporium,
Rivista Mensile D'Arte di Cultura*, Bergamo, Italy,
Aug. 1963, p. 95, illustrated.
Gift of Mrs. Frederick A. Geier in memory of
Emilie Esselborn Crane.

1958.93

1961.229

1961.229
ELDER OF THE APOCALYPSE, Castile, early
XIII c. Wood with polychromy, height 22¹⁵⁄₃₂ (67.2),
width of base 9¹¹⁄₃₂ (23.7), depth 7⁵⁄₁₆ (18.6).
Published: *The Art Quarterly*, xxv, 4, 1962, p. 407,
illustrated p. 397; *A Medieval Treasury*, Cornell
University, 1968, No. 62, pp. 6, 137.
Exhibited: *A Medieval Treasury*, Cornell, Munson-
Williams-Proctor Institute, 1968, No. 62.

1955.745
HEAD OF A BISHOP, Catalan, XIII c. Urgel
stone with polychromy, height 16⅝ (42.2), width
8⁹⁄₁₆ (21.7), depth 9³⁄₁₆ (23.3).
Published: *Cincinnati Art Museum Guide*, 1956, p.
14; José Pijoan, *Summa Artis, Historia General del
Arte*, Espasa-Calpe, S.A., Madrid, xi, 1947, p. 561,
fig. 902, 903; "Eleven Sculptured Heads,"
Columbus Gallery of Fine Arts Bulletin, vii, No. 5,
Feb. 1937.
Exhibited: *Eleven Sculptured Heads*, Columbus
Gallery of Fine Arts, 1937.
Collections: Kelekian, New York.
Gift of Piero Tozzi.

1945.67
VIRGIN AND CHILD, late XIV c. Alabaster,
height 18¹⁹⁄₃₂ (47.2), width 5⅞ (14.9), depth 4⁵⁄₁₆ (10.9).
Exhibited: *The Christmas Story*, Fort Wayne Art
School and Museum, Indiana, Nov. 29-Dec. 31, 1953;
Exhibition of Medieval Art, Columbus Gallery of
Fine Arts, Oct. 31-Nov. 22, 1958.
Gift of Mrs. Robert McKay.

1923.765
ST. ANDREW, XV c. Limestone with polychromy,
height 42⁵⁄₁₆ (107.5), width 15 (38.1), depth 8¼ (21.0).
Gift of Demotte, Inc.

1955.745

Europe and America after 1700

1966.39

Brazil

1946.47
MARTINS PEREIRA Y SOUSA, Maria (b. 1900), PLACE A L'IMPLACABLE, 1944. Bronze, height 29⅛ (74.0), width 45⅞ (116.5), depth 7⅜ (18.8)
Cf. Large version in the Museum of Modern Art, New York.
Anonymous gift.

England

1925.97
EPSTEIN, Sir Jacob (1880-1959), AN AMERICAN SOLDIER. Bronze, height 15⅞ (40.3), width 11⁷⁄₃₂ (28.5), depth 12 (30.5).
Gift of Dr. Samuel Rothenberg.

1966.39
EPSTEIN, Sir Jacob (1880-1959), PORTRAIT OF RABINDRANATH TAGORE. Bronze, height 19⁵⁄₁₆ (49.1), width 11⁷⁄₁₆ (29.0), depth 10¹³⁄₁₆ (27.5).
Gift of Mr. and Mrs. Leonard R. Minster.

France

1952.386
FALCONET, Etienne Maurice (1716-1791) and GOUTHIERE, Pierre (1732 or 1745-1813/14), CLOCK, figures by Falconet, ormolu by Gouthière, late XVIII c. Marble and bronze, height 25⅛ (63.8), width 19¼ (49.0), depth 9½ (24.2).
Published: Philip R. Adams, "The Anson Room," *Cincinnati Art Museum Bulletin*, I, 1, Oct. 1950, pp. 5-7; *Antiques*, LXXXIX, No. 3, Mar. 1966, illustrated p. 395.
Gift of Mrs. Alfred Anson.

1952.387
FALCONET, Etienne Maurice (1716-1791), LOVE'S TEACHING, late XVIII c. Marble, height without base 14⁵⁄₁₆ (35.7), width 6⅛ (5.5), depth 5⁷⁄₁₆ (13.6).
Published: Philip R. Adams, "The Anson Room," *Cincinnati Art Museum Bulletin*, Oct. 1950, pp. 5-7; *Antiques*, LXXXIX, No. 3, Mar. 1966, illustrated p. 395.
Gift of Mrs. Alfred Anson.

1952.388
FALCONET, Etienne Maurice (1716-1791), BATHER,
late XVIII c. Marble, height without base 14⅞ (37.8),
width 5¹³⁄₁₆ (14.7), depth 6⁷⁄₁₆ (16.4).
Published: Philip R. Adams, "The Anson Room,"
Cincinnati Art Museum Bulletin, I, 1, Oct. 1950,
pp. 5-6; *Cincinnati Art Museum Guide*, 1956, p. 80;
Antiques, LXXXIX, No. 3, Mar. 1966, p. 395,
illustrated p. 80.
Gift of Mrs. Alfred Anson.

1944.104
HOUDON, Jean Antoine (1741-1828), PORTRAIT OF
JEAN JACQUES ROUSSEAU, 1778. Plaster, height 27³⁄₁₆
(69.1), width 19⅜ (49.3), depth 11⅝ (29.5).
Inscribed: at the back under left shoulder, "J Jaqu";
under right shoulder "Houdo scul 1778."
Published: Walter H. Siple, *Cincinnati Art Museum
Newsnotes*, Jan. 1945; *Cincinnati Art Museum Guide*,
1956, p. 17; J. and T. Norman, *Traveler's Guide to
America's Art*, Meredith Press, New York, 1968, p. 332.
Gift of John J. Emery.

1944.104

1954.524
MARIN, Joseph Charles (1759-1834), BUST OF A YOUNG GIRL. Plaster, height with base 16¾ (42.5), without base 13¾ (35.0), width 8¹⁄₁₆ (20.5), depth 4⅞ (12.5). Signed at back "Marin, fecit."
Gift of the Duchess of Talleyrand-Perigord.

1949.145
DEGAS, Hilaire Germain Edgar (1834-1917), BALLERINA. Bronze, height 23³⁄₁₆ (56.3), width tip of right hand to left armpit 11¹⁄₁₆ (28.1), depth from tip of right foot to right hip 12¹³⁄₁₆ (32.6).
Inscribed: back right of base, "Degas," stamped left back of base, "5/D CIRE PERDUE A A HEBRARD."
Exhibited: *Nineteenth Century Painting and Sculpture,* Seattle Art Museum, Mar. 7-May 6, 1951.
Gift of Mr. and Mrs. John J. Emery.

1955.527
RODIN, Auguste (1840-1917), LION, 1881. Plaster, height 11¹⁄₁₆ (28.1), width 6⅛ (15.5), depth 13¹⁄₁₆ (33.2).
Inscribed: on band, *"Garde bien"*; to right of lion's right paw, "1881, 21 Mai."
This plaster sketch is a study for a Franco-Prussian war memorial which was never executed.
Gift of Lucien Wulsin.

1958.476
RODIN, Auguste (1840-1917), THE EVIL SPIRITS, (Les mauvais génies), 1886. Bronze, height 12¹³⁄₁₆ (32.5), width 7¹⁵⁄₁₆ (20.2), depth 8⅜ (21.2).
Inscribed: back right, "A. Rodin, 86"; back, "Alexis. Rudier Fondeur, Paris."
Published: Georges Grappe, *Catalogue du Musée Rodin,* Paris, 1944, No. 307.
Collections: Mary Hanna, Cincinnati.
Gift of John B. Hollister.

1956.404
RODIN, Auguste (1840-1917), MALE TORSO. Bronze, height, 10½ (26.7), width, 7⁵⁄₁₆ (18.6), depth 3⅞ (9.8).
Inscribed: right side of base, "A. Rodin."
This small bronze is based on the torso of Rodin's first major success, the life-size "Age d'Airin."
Exhibited: *Rodin,* The Museum of Modern Art, New York, Apr. 29-Sept. 10, 1963, No. 56; *Rodin,* California Palace of the Legion of Honor, Oct. 19-Dec. 8, 1963, No. 82.
Gift of Mr. and Mrs. Lucien Wulsin.

1949.145

1956.404

1936.8
CARLES, Jean-Antonin (1851-1919), La Jeunesse. Bronze, height $10\frac{29}{32}$ (27.7), width at elbows $3\frac{5}{8}$ (9.3), diameter of base $2\frac{7}{16}$ (6.1).
Inscribed: right side of base, "ANTONIN CARLES IS"; front of base, "LA JEUNESSE"; back of base, "SIOT. DECAUVILLE, FONDEUR, PARIS."
Gift of Mrs. George Warrington.

1963.12
LACHAISE, Gaston (1886-1935), Mask, 1928, Lead, height $7\frac{13}{16}$ (19.8), width $5\frac{11}{16}$ (14.4), depth $3\frac{5}{16}$ (8.4).
Inscribed: on back, "Lachaise 1928."
Exhibited: *Gaston Lachaise—Sculpture and Drawings,* Los Angeles County Museum of Art, Dec. 3, 1963-Jan. 19, 1964; Whitney Museum of American Art, New York, Feb. 18-Apr. 5, 1964, cat. No. 73, illustrated.
Gift of Dr. and Mrs. J. Louis Ransohoff.

1963.2
HILBERT, Georges (b. 1900), Bulldog, 1926. Grey granite, height $15\frac{3}{4}$ (40.0), width $9\frac{15}{16}$ (25.2), depth $23\frac{3}{8}$ (59.3).
Gift of Mrs. Ralph Robertson.

1958.550
KNOOP, Guitou (b. 1902), Double Image. Limestone, height $27\frac{7}{16}$ (69.2), width 32 (81.2), depth $15\frac{1}{16}$ (38.3).
Gift of Henri Doll.

Germany

1952.198
KRELING, August von (1819-1876), Model for Tyler Davidson Fountain, 1869. Bronze, height $41\frac{1}{4}$ (114.7), width $29\frac{15}{16}$ (76.1), depth $29\frac{9}{16}$ (75.6).
The original model for the fountain in Fountain Square, Cincinnati. Some details of the base were altered between the model stage and the actual fountain when finished.
Collections: From the artist to Henry Probasco to Isaac Graveson, to Harry Booth, to Eugene Booth.
Bequest of Eugene Booth.

1967.1262
LEDERER, Hugo (1871-1940), Portrait of Marguerite Melville Liszniewska, 1930. Bronze, height $15\frac{7}{16}$ (39.2), width $8\frac{3}{8}$ (21.2), depth $10\frac{3}{8}$ (26.4).
Inscribed: back of neck, "Hugo Lederer 1930."
Gift of John H. Melville.

Italy

1891.7
GUGLIELMI, Luigi (1834-1907). Portrait of Mrs. Mills. Marble, height $30\frac{1}{2}$ (77.5) with base, width $17\frac{1}{4}$ (43.8), depth $9\frac{3}{4}$ (24.7).
Inscribed: on back "L. GUGLIELMI F. ROMA."
Published: *Catalog of Oil Paintings and Sculpture in the Art Museum,* Cincinnati, 1904, 1905, S.13.
Gift of the executors of the Estate of Reuben R. Springer.

1953.63
MARINI, Marino (b. 1901), Kneeling Nude, 1945. Bronze, height $16\frac{7}{16}$ (41.8), width $9\frac{13}{16}$ (24.9), depth $9\frac{3}{4}$ (24.7).
Inscribed : on right foot, "M.M."
Published: Umbro Apollonio, *Marino Marini,* Milan, 2nd edition revised, No. 59, illustrated.
Gift of the Cincinnati Modern Art Society.

United States

1957.150
ECKSTEIN, Frederick (1775-1852), Marquis de Lafayette, 1825. Plaster, height $22\frac{19}{16}$ (57.3), width $13\frac{3}{16}$ (33.5), depth $9\frac{13}{16}$ (24.9), height of base $6\frac{17}{32}$ (16.6).
Eckstein settled in Cincinnati in 1823 and was Hiram Powers' first teacher. This portrait was said to have been done from life when Lafayette visited Cincinnati in 1825. Cf. Craven, *Sculpture in America,* 1968, p. 111.
Published: *Bulletin,* Cincinnati Historical Society, Jan. 1967, XXV, 1, p. 16 illustrated.
Collections: John Hough James, Urbana, Ohio; John Henry James, Urbana, Ohio; Margaret James, Urbana, Ohio.

1916.288
ECKSTEIN, Frederick (1775-1852), Resurrection of Jarius. Wax relief, height $20\frac{3}{4}$ (52.5) width $31\frac{1}{4}$ (79.4), depth $7\frac{7}{8}$ (20.0).
Gift of Frances Eckstein.

1916.287
ECKSTEIN, Frederick (1775-1852), RESURRECTION
OF LAZARUS. Wax relief, height 20¾ (52.8), width
31¼ (79.4), depth ca. 6⅞ (17.5).
Gift of Frances Eckstein.

1965.4
POWERS, Hiram (1805-1873), PORTRAIT OF MINER
KILBOURNE KELLOGG, 1828. Wax tinted to look like
bronze, height 10⅝ (27.0), width 4¾ (12.1), depth
4½ (11.4).
Paper label imitating bronze plate on front of base:
"M. K. Kellogg aged 14 years. The first Bust by
Hiram Powers Cincinnati, Ohio 1828."
Published: *The Art Quarterly*, XXVIII, 4 1965, p.
315, illustrated p. 322; *Cincinnati Art Museum
Bulletin*, VIII, 1, Feb. 1966, p. 17 illustrated; Llerena
Friend, *M. K. Kellogg's Texas Journal, 1872*, Uni-
versity of Texas Press, 1967, between pp. 34 and 35.
Gift of Paul G. Pennoyer.

1888.86
POWERS, Hiram (1805-1873), EVE DISCONSOLATE,
1855-1860. Marble, height 76³⁄₁₆ (193.5) diameter
of base 22¹⁄₁₆ (56.0).
Inscribed: back of base, "H. Powers, Sculp." front,
"H.P.-N.L."
Published: *Catalog of Oil Paintings and Sculpture in
the Art Museum*, Cincinnati, 1888, 1890, S.98; 1898,
1904, 1905, S.1; Henry Boynton, *Hiram Powers*,
Boston, W. B. Clarke Co., 1899, p. 527; Lorado Taft,
American Sculpture, New York, Macmillan, 1930,
pp. 66-67; Nathalia Wright, *American Novelists in
Italy; The Discoverers: Allston to James*, University
of Pennsylvania Press, 1965, illustrated p. 151;
Craven, *Sculpture in America*, 1968, p. 120.
Exhibited: *Exhibition of Paintings by Joseph Oriel
Eaton and Sculpture by Hiram Powers*, Cincinnati
Art Museum, 1934, No. 74.
Gift of Nicholas Longworth.

1888.86

1884.394
POWERS, Hiram (1805-1873), PROSERPINE, sometimes
called EVANGELINE, 1844. Marble, height with base
24¹⁵⁄₁₆ (63.3), width 19¹⁄₁₆ (48.5), depth 11³⁄₁₆ (28.7).
Inscribed: back, "H. POWERS Sc. 1844."
Published: *Catalog of Oil Paintings and Sculpture in
the Art Museum*, Cincinnati, 1888, 1890, S.56; 1898,
1904, 1905, S.2; Henry Boynton, *Hiram Powers*,
Boston, W. B. Clarke Co., 1899, p. 530; *Cincinnati
Museum Review of the Collections*, 1924, fig. 3;
Lorado Taft, *American Sculpture*, New York,
Macmillan, 1930, p. 61, fig. 6.
Exhibited: *Exhibition of Paintings by Joseph Oriel
Eaton and Sculpture by Hiram Powers*, Cincinnati
Art Museum, 1934, No. 84.
Gift of Reuben R. Springer.

1893.63
POWERS, Hiram (1805-1873), GINEVRA. Marble,
height with base 29¹⁵⁄₁₆ (76.0), width 18³⁄₈ (46.7), depth
11 (28.0).

Inscribed: DEDICATED BY THE AUTHOR, TO HIS
FRIEND AND PATRON N. LONGWORTH,
ESQ. HIRAM POWERS, SCULP."
Published: *Catalog of Oil Paintings and Sculpture
in the Art Museum*, Cincinnati, 1904, 1905, S.14;
Henry Boynton, *Hiram Powers*, Boston, W. B. Clarke
Co., 1899, p. 531; Craven, *Sculpture in America*,
1968, p. 115.
Exhibited: Cincinnati Industrial Exposition, 1872,
No. 3; *Exhibition of Paintings by Joseph Oriel Eaton
and Sculpture by Hiram Powers*, Cincinnati Art
Museum, 1934, No. 77.
Gift of the heirs of Catherine Anderson.

1907.287
POWERS, Hiram (1805-1873), GREEK SLAVE. Marble,
height 20¹⁄₁₆ (51.0), width 15⁵⁄₃₂ (38.5), depth 8⁷⁄₃₂ (20.9).
This is a smaller bust version of the celebrated
full-length figure.
Inscribed: back, "H. POWERS."
Published: Samuel A. Robertson and William H.
Gerdts, "The Greek Slave," *The Museum*, Newark
Museum, XVII, 1-2, Winter-Spring 1965, fig. 19 and
p. 25; Richard J. Boyle, "Miner Kilbourne Kellogg,"
Cincinnati Art Museum Bulletin, VIII, 1, Feb. 1966,
pp. 20, 22, fig. 9.
Exhibited: *Exhibition of Paintings by Joseph Oriel
Eaton and Sculpture by Hiram Powers*, Cincinnati,
1934, No. 80.
Gift of W. G. Hosea.

1891.1
POWERS, Hiram (1805-1873), PSYCHE. Marble,
height 25³⁄₁₆ (64.0), width 18¹⁄₂ (46.9), depth 10¹⁄₈ (25.7).
Published: *Catalog of Oil Paintings and Sculpture in
the Art Museum*, Cincinnati, 1888, 1890, S.57;
1898, 1904, 1905, S.3.
Exhibited: *Exhibition of Paintings by Joseph Oriel
Eaton and Sculpture by Hiram Powers*, Cincinnati
Art Museum, 1934, No. 85; "*American Heritage*,"
Columbus Gallery of Fine Arts, Oct. 9-Nov. 28, 1949;
American Masters of Sculpture, Herron Museum of
Art, Indianapolis, 1963, No. 2.
Gift of Charles Dexter.

1935.321
POWERS, Hiram (1805-1873), PORTRAIT OF GEORGE
WASHINGTON. Marble, height with base 30⁵⁄₁₆ (77.0)

width 24¹⁄₁₆ (61.1), depth 14¹⁄₁₆ (35.7).
Inscribed: back, "H. POWERS Sculp."
Exhibited: *Exhibition of Paintings by Joseph Oriel Eaton and Sculpture by Hiram Powers*, Cincinnati Art Museum, 1934, No. 89.
Bequest of Dr. Derrick T. Vail, Sr.

1935.322
POWERS, Hiram (1805-1873), PORTRAIT OF BENJAMIN FRANKLIN. Marble, height with base 26⅛ (66.3), width 17⅜ (44.1), depth 9⁷⁄₁₆ (24.6).
Inscribed: back, "H. POWERS Sculp."
Exhibited: *Exhibition of Paintings by Joseph Oriel Eaton and Sculpture by Hiram Powers*, Cincinnati Art Museum, 1934, No. 76.
Bequest of Dr. Derrick T. Vail, Sr.

1954.112
POWERS, Hiram (1805-1873), PORTRAIT OF NICHOLAS LONGWORTH. Marble, height 19²¹⁄₃₂ (50.0), width 13½ (34.3), depth 8⁹⁄₁₆ (21.7).
Inscribed: back, "HIRAM POWERS. Sculp."
Published: *The Art Quarterly*, Autumn 1954, p. 303, No. 2, illustrated; *Museum Echoes*, Ohio Historical Society, Columbus, Ohio, XXXIII, 8; Craven, *Sculpture in America*, 1968, p. 113.
Exhibited: *Exhibition of Paintings by Joseph Oriel Eaton and Sculpture by Hiram Powers*, Cincinnati Art Museum, 1934, No. 81.
Gift of Alice Roosevelt Longworth and Paulina Longworth Sturm.

1941.8
POWERS, Hiram (1805-1873), PORTRAIT OF JUDGE JACOB BURNET. Marble, height with base 25¹⁹⁄₁₆ (65.0), width 14½ (36.8), depth 8⅝ (22.9).
Inscribed: back, "HIRAM POWERS. Sculp."
Published: *Catalog of Oil Paintings and Sculpture in the Art Museum*, Cincinnati, 1904, 1905, S.69.
Exhibited: *Exhibition of Paintings by Joseph Oriel Eaton and Sculpture by Hiram Powers*, Cincinnati Art Museum, 1934, No. 73.
Gift of Mrs. Daniel Riker.

1897.32
POWERS, Hiram (1805-1873), PORTRAIT OF JAMES GILMORE, 1865. Marble, height 26⁹⁄₁₆ (67.5), width 15²¹⁄₃₂ (39.8), depth 9⅝ (24.5).

Inscribed: back, "James Gilmore, aged 51 Hiram Powers sculp. 1865."
Published: *Catalog of Oil Paintings and Sculpture in the Art Museum*, Cincinnati, 1904, 1905, S.20; Craven, *Sculpture in America*, 1968, p. 122.
Exhibited: *Exhibition of Paintings by Joseph Oriel Eaton and Sculpture by Hiram Powers*, Cincinnati Art Museum, 1934, No. 78; *American Masters of Sculpture*, Herron Museum of Art, Indianapolis, 1965, No. 1, illustrated.
Gift of the Estate of James Gilmore.

1941.214
KING, John Crookshanks (1806-1882), PORTRAIT OF ROBERT BURNS, 1859. Marble, height 25 (63.5), width 19½ (49.5), depth 14 (35.6).
Inscribed: "J. C. King Sculp 1859."
King, born in Scotland, emigrated to the United States in 1829. Between about 1832 and 1836 he was active in Cincinnati where he studied with Hiram Powers. Cf. Craven, *Sculpture in America*, 1968, p. 191.
Gift of Mrs. Charles L. Mitchell.

1954.112

1913.97
IVES, Chauncey Bradley (1810-1894), PORTRAIT OF NATHANIEL GREEN PENDLETON, Rome 1858. Marble, height 33 (83.7) with base, width 21¼ (54.0), depth 9¾ (24.8).
Inscribed: "C.B. Ives, Rome 1858."
Exhibited: *American Masters of Sculpture*, Herron Museum of Art, Indianapolis, 1965, No. 3, illustrated.
Gift of Mrs. Margaret Riviere Pendleton.

1954.3
WILSON, Caroline (Mrs. Israel) (1810-1890), MARY MAGDALENE, Cincinnati, 1860. Marble, height 36¼ (92.1), width 28⅜ (72.1), depth 30½ (77.5).
Inscribed: base "LET HER ALONE AGAINST THE DAY OF MY BURYING HATH SHE KEPT THIS JOHN 12 CAROLINE WILSON, CIN., 1860."
This figure was given to Lane Seminary, Cincinnati, by the artist in 1875.
Published: Lane Seminary *Minutes*, Vol. IV, 1875, pp. 82-83; Vol. V, 1887, pp. 376-377; Henry A. and Kate B. Ford, *History of Cincinnati, Ohio*, Williams Printing House, Cleveland, 1881, p. 242.
Gift of Lane Seminary per William E. Dean.

1885.12
WILSON, Caroline (Mrs. Israel) (1810-1890), PORTRAIT OF THE REV. LYMAN A. BEECHER, 1860, Cincinnati. Marble, height 29²¹⁄₃₂ (75.3), width 19¼ (48.8), depth 9½ (24.1).
Inscribed: back, "MRS. WILSON, ARTISTE CIN. O."; front, "LYMAN BEECHER D.D. CIN. 1860."
Mrs. Wilson probably made her original studies for this portrait before 1850 when Lyman Beecher moved to New York.
Published: *Catalog of Oil Paintings and Sculpture in the Art Museum*, Cincinnati, 1888, 1890, S.59; 1898, 1904, 1905, S.9.
Exhibited: Harriet Beecher Stowe House, Cincinnati, June 1948-April 1961.
Gift of the artist.

1918.4
JONES, Thomas Dow (1811-1881), BUST OF GRIFFIN TAYLOR. Marble, height 32⁵⁄₁₆ (82.6), width 21¹⁵⁄₁₆ (55.7), depth 14⁵⁄₁₆ (36.4).
Jones was active in Cincinnati 1841-1850 and again after 1865.

Published: Craven, *Sculpture in America*, 1968, p. 202, Fig. 6.11.
Gift of Mary Kilgour Miller, Edmond C. Miller and Rufus King.

1944.3
CLEVENGER, Shobal Vail (1812-1843), BUST OF JOSIAH LAWRENCE. Plaster, height 21¹⁄₁₆ (53.5), width 17¼ (43.8), depth 8½ (21.6).
Inscribed: on back of base, "S.V. Clevenger 1837."
Josiah Lawrence was a resident of Middletown, Ohio, where Clevenger was born and brought up, until he moved to Cincinnati around 1826. Lawrence was the great-grandfather of the donor.
Published: Thomas B. Brumbaugh, "Shobal Clevenger, An Ohio Stonecutter in Search of Fame," *The Art Quarterly*, XXIX, 1, 1966, p. 45, note 40; Craven, *Sculpture in America*, 1968, p. 182, fig. 6.1.
Gift of Lawrence Minor.

1885.12

1924.263 and 1924.459
FRANKENSTEIN, John P. (1817-1881), PORTRAIT OF JUDGE JOHN MCLEAN, Cincinnati. 1924.263: plaster, height 24 9/16 (62.4), width 22 9/32 (54.1), depth 12 5/16 (31.2). 1924.459: bronze, same dimensions. The plaster version from which the bronze was cast as a gift of George W. Armstrong in 1924, is believed to have entered the Museum in 1884 with other effects of the McMicken School of Art which was absorbed by the Cincinnati Art Academy in that year. It should be noted in this connection that Mrs. John McLean was associated in 1854 with the founding of the Cincinnati Academy of Fine Arts, later absorbed into the McMicken School of Design of the University. Another plaster version exists in the Mercantile Library, Cincinnati, and is presumably the one referred to by Frankenstein himself in his *American Art Its Awful Altitude*, 1864. Frankenstein was active in Cincinnati about 1831-1839 and again 1856-1864.
Published: William Coyle, *The Frankenstein Family in Springfield*, Clark County Historical Society, Springfield, Ohio, 1967, pl. 2 (bronze).

1969.385
BALL, Thomas (1819-1911), PAUL REVERE. Bronze, height 33 1/8 (84.1), width 12 1/4 (31:1), depth 42 3/4 (108.6).
Inscribed: side of base below left fore foot, "T. BALL. Sculp. 1883"; left side of base, "PAUL REVERE"; side of base below right hind leg, "Fonderia Papi via Flli Galli Firenze."
The Edwin and Virginia Irwin Memorial.

1919.155
BAKER, Nathan Foster (1820-1891), PORTRAIT OF JAMES KEYS WILSON. Marble, height 21 (53.3), width 18 3/8 (46.7), depth 9 1/8 (23.2).
James Keys Wilson (1828-1894) was the architect responsible for such Victorian monuments in Cincinnati as Scarlet Oaks (the Schoenberger mansion), the Isaac M. Wise Temple and the gatehouse of Spring Grove Cemetery.
Published: Craven, *Sculpture in America*, 1968, p. 189.
Gift of Henry Neill Wilson.

1914.14
RINEHART, William Henry (1825-1874), PORTRAIT OF JAMES A. FRAZER. Marble, height 29 1/2 (74.9), width 20 (50.8), depth 12 3/4 (32.4).
Published: *Catalog of Oil Paintings and Sculpture in the Art Museum*, Cincinnati, 1890, 1898, 1904, 1905, S.58.
Bequest of Mrs. Eliza McCormick Frazer.

1888.293
ROGERS, Randolph (1825-1892), THE LAST ARROW (THE LAST OF HIS TRIBE). Bronze, height 43 3/4 (111.0), with 18 3/4 (47.5), depth 53 1/8 (135.0).
Inscribed: front of base, "RANDOLPH ROGERS ROME," "FONDERIA NELLI ROMA."
Published: *Catalog of Oil Paintings and Sculpture in the Art Museum, Cincinnati*, 1888, 1890, S.103; 1898, 1904, 1905, S.10.
Gift of O. J. Wilson.

1964.346
ROGERS, Randolph (1825-1892), HEAD OF A LITTLE GIRL. Marble, height 21 1/16 (53.4), width 14 3/4 (37.5), depth 9 5/8 (24.5).
Inscribed: back of base, "Randolph Rögers, Roma."
Gift of Webb and Stacy Hill in memory of Mr. and Mrs. Webb Hill.

1957.220
WEBBER, Charles T. (1825-1911), PORTRAIT OF H. CHANE MILLER, Cincinnati, 1896. Bronze relief, height 26 (66.0), width 19 1/2 (49.5), depth (average thickness) 13/16 (1.0).
Inscriptions: Two scores of music above man's profile with the words, "I Love to Tell the Story"; below, "Director of Cincinnati House of Refuge 1864-1895; C. T. Webber 1896; Donated by R. A. Holden"; lower right corner, "Cast by Alex. Reigler, Central Bronze Works."
Webber, who settled in Cincinnati in 1858, was primarily a painter but occasionally turned his hand to portrait sculpture. He is best known for his painting, "The Underground Railway."
Gift of Ohio College of Applied Science.

1911.1373
WEBBER, Charles T. (1825-1911), PORTRAIT OF CHRISTINE SULLIVAN, Cincinnati, 1901. Marble, height 26 3/4 (68.0), width 19 1/16 (48.4), depth 12 1/4 (31.1).
Inscribed: left side of base, "C. T. Webber Cinti. 1901"; front of base, "Christine Sullivan."
Gift of Arthur Owen Jones.

1910.564
VOLK, Leonard Wells (1828-1895), Bust of Abraham
Lincoln. Bronze, height 24¼ (61.6), width 15⅞ (40.4),
depth 10 (25.4).
Gift of Jules Bercham.

X1962.27
ROGERS, John (1829-1904), Taking the Oath and
Drawing Rations. Painted plaster, height 23³⁄₁₆ (58.8),
width at base 12¹³⁄₁₆ (32.5), depth at base 8⅞ (22.5).
Inscribed: top of base, "JOHN ROGERS NEW YORK";
front of base, "TAKING THE OATH AND DRAWING
RATIONS"; back of base, "PATENTED JAN31 1866."

1963.818
ROGERS, John (1829-1904), Private Theatricals—
Last Moments Behind the Scenes, New York, 1878.
Painted plaster, height 23⅞ (60.7), width 19⅞ (50.5),
depth 11¹⁵⁄₁₆ (30.3)
Inscribed: top of base, "JOHN ROGERS NEW YORK
1878"; front of base, "PRIVATE THEATRICALS—
LAST MOMENTS BEHIND THE SCENES."
Gift of Mrs. Robert Stevie.

X1967.4
ROGERS, John (1829-1904), The Fugitive's Story,
New York. Plaster, height 21⅞ (55.5), width of base
15¹⁵⁄₁₆ (40.5), depth of base 12 (30.5).
Inscribed: top of base, "JOHN ROGERS NEW YORK";
front, "THE FUGITIVE'S STORY JOHN C. WHITTIER—
H. W. BEECHER—WM. LLOYD GARRISON."

1884.410
ROGERS, John (1829-1904), Wounded to the Rear
—One More Shot, New York. White biscuit, height
20 (50.7), diameter of base 8⁷⁄₁₆ (21.5).
Inscribed: on the bag, "JOHN ROGERS NEW YORK";
on front of base, "WOUNDED TO THE REAR—
ONE MORE SHOT."
Cf. Lorado Taft, *The History of American Sculpture*,
Macmillan, N. Y., 1903, p. 185, fig. 25; Albert Ten
Eyck Gardner, *American Sculpture*, Metropolitan
Museum, New York, 1965, pp. 29-30.
Bequest of Reuben R. Springer.

1951.181
BULLETT, Charles (d. 1875), Bust of Samuel N.
Pike, Cincinnati, ca. 1850-60. Marble, height 24¼

(61.3) without base, width 19½ (48.5), depth
12⅞ (32.7).
Very little is known about this artist who was
active in Cincinnati in the 1850's, but a collateral
branch of the family in Newport, Ky., believes that
he was buried at Cave Hill Cemetery, Louisville,
Ky., which does indeed have record of a Charles
Bullett buried there in 1875. Samuel N. Pike, 1822-
1872, was a philanthropist, civic leader and art
patron who built the first opera house in the West
at Cincinnati.
Gift of Mrs. L. D. and Miss N. C. Barney and
Mrs. Ellen Rionda.

1921.502

1896.4
BULLETT, Charles (d. 1875), BUST OF MRS. SARAH WORTHINGTON KING PETER, 1854. Marble, height with base $26\frac{1}{8}$ (66.4), width $18\frac{7}{16}$ (48.8), depth $11\frac{1}{8}$ (28.3).
Inscribed: back, "C. Bullett 1854."
Mrs. Peter was the daughter of Thomas Worthington, Governor of and Senator from Ohio. In 1854 she led a group of ladies to form the Cincinnati Academy of Fine Arts from which both the Cincinnati Art Museum and the Cincinnati Art Academy derive.
Published: *Catalog of Oil Paintings and Sculpture in the Art Museum,* Cincinnati, 1888, 1890, S. 97; 1904, 1905, S. 19; Margaret R. King, *Memoirs of the Life of Mrs. Sarah Peter,* Cincinnati, Robert Clarke & Co., 1889, II, frontispiece.
Exhibited: *Cincinnati Women,* Historical Society of Ohio, Taft Museum, Cincinnati, Apr. 22-June 8, 1954.
Gift of Mrs. Rufus King.

1921.502
WARD, John Quincy Adams (1830-1910), THE EMANCIPATED SLAVE, 1863. Bronze, height $19\frac{5}{8}$ (49.8), width at base $14\frac{5}{8}$ (37.1), depth at base $7\frac{1}{8}$ (18.1).
Inscribed: "J. Q. A. WARD. SC. 1863."
Published: *The Indianapolis Star,* section 10, p. 5, Oct. 10, 1965, illustrated.
Exhibited: Harriet Beecher Stowe House, Cincinnati, June 9, 1949—April 26, 1961; *American Masters of Sculpture,* Herron Museum of Art, Indianapolis, 1965, No. 8, illustrated.
Gift of Mrs. Howard Hollister and Mary Eva Keys.

1957.151
WARD, John Quincy Adams (1830-1910), SIMON KENTON, THE INDIAN FIGHTER. Plaster, height $27\frac{5}{16}$ (69.35), width $11\frac{1}{16}$ (28.1), depth $8\frac{7}{8}$ (22.6).
Study for proposed monument in Urbana, Ohio.
Collections: John H. James, Urbana, Ohio; Margaret James, Urbana, Ohio.

1884.542
PARK, Richard Henry (1832-after 1890), MIGNON. Marble, height $47\frac{5}{8}$ (121.0), width $23\frac{11}{16}$ (60.2), depth $21\frac{1}{8}$ (53.5).
Inscribed: "R.H. Park."
Published: *Catalog of Oil Paintings and Sculpture in the Art Museum,* Cincinnati, 1888, 1890, S.65; 1898, 1904, 1905, S.4; *Cincinnati Museum Review of the Collections,* 1924, figs. 3, 20.
Gift of Mr. and Mrs. J. G. Schmidlapp.

1956.246
REBISSO, Louis T. (1837-1899), HIRAM BANKS HALSTEAD, ca. 1877. Bronze, height $21\frac{7}{8}$ (55.6), width 12 (30.5), depth $8\frac{3}{8}$ (21.2).
Rebisso, born in Genoa, came to Cincinnati about 1870 and from about 1874 on was an instructor at the McMicken School of Design, transferring with it to the Art Academy of Cincinnati in 1884. After his death he was succeeded on the faculty by Clement J. Barnhorn.
Exhibited: *Loan Exhibition of Portraits in the Art Galleries of Music Hall, Cincinnati, for the Benefit of Laura Memorial College and Hospital,* 1896, No. 591.
Collections: Mr. and Mrs. Murat Halstead, 1896.
Gift of Mrs. Jesse Clark.

1934.73
BAKER, Davis, mid XIX c., PORTRAIT OF MRS. WILLIAM WOOLSEY SCARBOROUGH (1822-1902). Marble, height $29\frac{1}{4}$ (74.3), width $18\frac{1}{4}$ (46.3), depth $10\frac{1}{4}$ (26.0).
Gift of Rebecca Scarborough and Mrs. Hugh Smythe.

1908.39
CONNELLY, Pierce Francis (1841-after 1902), BUST OF A YOUNG WOMAN, 1865. Marble, height $23\frac{3}{16}$ (56.3), width $19\frac{1}{8}$ (48.6), depth $9\frac{1}{8}$ (23.1).
Inscribed: back, "P.F. CONNELLY. FECIT FLOR. 1865."
Gift of Mrs. L. B. Harrison.

1952.66
EZEKIEL, Moses J. (1844-1917), JUDITH. Marble, height $30\frac{7}{8}$ (78.3), width $18\frac{5}{16}$ (46.5), depth $15\frac{9}{16}$ (39.5).
Ezekiel spent about a year in Cincinnati around 1868 studying with J. Insco Williams and Thomas Dow Jones, but his period of great popularity came after he settled in Rome.
Published: *Catalog of Oil Paintings and Sculpture in the Art Museum,* Cincinnati, 1898, 1904, 1905, S.63; Joseph Gutmann, "Jewish Participation in the Visual Arts of 18th and 19th Century America," *American Jewish Archives,* Apr. 1963, XV, 1, p. 45.
Bequest of Margaret Rives Nichols, Marquise de Chambrun.

1902.6
EZEKIEL, Moses J. (1844-1917), ECCE HOMO.
Bronze, height 21⅝ (54.9), width 17¹³⁄₁₆ (43.3), depth
16¹¹⁄₁₆ (42.4).
Not signed or dated, but probably contemporary with
a slightly different version dated 1899 which was
sold out of his son Henry's collection in 1930.
Published: Craven, *Sculpture in America*, 1968,
p. 338.
Gift of Harry W. Levy and George W. Harris.

X1963.1
EZEKIEL, Moses J. (1844-1917). PORTRAIT OF
BELLAMY STORER. Marble, height 22⅝ (57.5), width
14¹⁄₁₆ (35.7), depth 9⁹⁄₁₆ (24.3).
Anonymous gift.

1911.611
EZEKIEL, Moses J. (1844-1917), PORTRAIT OF MRS.
CHARLES MILLS. Marble relief, height 21⁹⁄₁₆ (54.8),
width 15²⁹⁄₃₂ (40.4), depth 2³⁄₃₂ (5.3)
Published: *Catalog of Oil Paintings and Sculpture in
the Art Museum*, Cincinnati, 1898, 1904, 1905, S.67.
Gift of Charles L. Mills.

1962.490
EZEKIEL, Moses, J. (1844-1917). HEAD OF A LITTLE
GIRL, 1895. Marble, height 21¼ (53.9), width 15¹⁵⁄₃₂
(39.3), depth 9¼ (23.5).
Inscribed: back of base, "M.Ezekiel Roma 1895."
Gift of Mr. and Mrs. Martin Low.

1889.516
EZEKIEL, Moses J. (1844-1917), BUST OF LONGFELLOW.
Marble, height 38 (96.5) with base, width 22½ (57.2),
depth 17¾ (45.1).
Published: *Catalog of Oil Paintings and Sculpture
in the Art Museum*, Cincinnati, 1890, S.116; 1898,
1904, 1905, S.7; Henry K. Bush-Brown, "Sir Moses
Ezekiel: American Sculptor," *Art & Archaeology*,
XI, 6, June 1921, illus. in photo of Ezekiel's studio
in Rome.
Gift of Mrs. M. L. Schmidlapp.

1888.331
BARBEE, Herbert (1848- ?), PORTRAIT OF JAMES
W. MCLAUGHLIN. Marble, height 29¾ (75.5), width
17¹⁵⁄₁₆ (45.5), depth 11⅝ (29.5).

James W. McLaughlin was the architect of the
Museum's original building, opened on May 17, 1886.
Published: *Catalog of Oil Paintings and Sculpture in
the Art Museum*, Cincinnati, 1890, S.108; 1898, 1904,
1905, S.10.
Exhibited: *Cincinnati Industrial Exposition*, 1886,
No. 330.
Gift of Gen. A. Hickenlooper, A. W. Whelpley
and John C. Riley.

1940.1206
SAINT-GAUDENS, Augustus (1848-1907), AMOR
CARITAS. Bronze, height 39¾ (101.0), width 16¹³⁄₁₆
(42.7), depth 4½ (11.5).
Inscribed: top center, "AMOR CARITAS"; lower left,
"AVGVSTVS SAINTGAVDENS MDCCCXCVIII".
A reduced version of the bronze in the
Luxembourg Museum.
Gift of Mrs. Charles S. Hofer.

1955.795
SAINT-GAUDENS, Augustus (1848-1907),
STANLEY MATTHEWS AND HIS WIFE MARY. Bronze
portrait relief, height 32⅝ (83.0), width 47 (119.5),
depth 1 (2.5).
Inscribed: upper right corner, "STANLEY MATTHEWS
AND HIS WIFE MARY"; lower left, "ASPEY MCMIV";
lower right, AUBRY BROS CO NEW YORK 1904."
Published: S. Lewis Hind, *Augustus Saint-Gaudens*,
New York, 1908, p. xlv.
Gift. of T. S. Matthews.

1895.146
DUVENECK, Frank (1848-1919), and BARNHORN,
Clement J. (1857-1935), MEMORIAL TO ELIZABETH
BOOTT DUVENECK, 1891. Plaster, height 28¾ (73.0),
length 85⁹⁄₁₆ (217.3), width 40¹³⁄₃₂ (102.6).
Inscribed: "Frank Duveneck—1891."
Plaster study for bronze memorial in the
Allori Cemetery, Florence, Italy. Duveneck was
primarily a painter but collaborated with Barnhorn
on a few works of sculpture. Both were instructors
at the Art Academy of Cincinnati.
Published: *American Sculpture*, Metropolitan
Museum of Art, New York, 1965, p. 96; Nathalia
Wright, *American Novelists in Italy: The
Discoverers: Allston to James*, University of
Pennsylvania Press, 1965, p. 259 illustrated.

Exhibited: *Loan Exhibition of Portraits in the Art Galleries of Music Hall, Cincinnati, for the Benefit of Laura Memorial College and Hospital*, 1896, No. 776; Barnhorn Exhibition 1934, No. 1.
Gift of Frank Duveneck.

1905.211
DUVENECK, Frank (1848-1919), and BARNHORN, Clement J. (1857-1935), RALPH WALDO EMERSON, 1905.
Plaster, height 56⅚₁₆ (143.0), width 35⁷⁄₁₆ (90.0), depth 45¼ (115.0).
Original cast of heroic-size figure for bronze seated figure at Harvard University.
Published: *Cincinnati Museum Review of the Collections*, 1924, fig. 19.
Gift of the artists.

1955.795

1895.146

1963.533
MUNDHENK, August (1848-1922), PORTRAIT OF
JOHN STRAUS, Cincinnati. Plaster, diameter 19¾ (50.2).
The subject was the father of the donors. Mundhenk
studied at the Cincinnati Art Academy and was
an associate of Louis T. Rebisso.
Gift of Mrs. Henry Englander and Mrs.
Jessie Straus Meyer.

1882.232
KEYSER, Ephraim (1850-1937), PSYCHE. Marble,
height 56 (142.3), width 18¾ (47.7), depth 22³⁄₁₆ (56.4).
Inscribed: "E. Keyser mod. Berlin '77 Fec. Rome '78."
Published: *Catalog of Oil Paintings and Sculpture in
the Art Museum*, Cincinnati, 1888, 1890, S.86; 1898,
1904, 1905, S.6; *Cincinnati Museum Review of the
Collections*, 1924, fig. 3; Thieme-Becker, *Künstler-
Lexicon*, 1938, Vol. XX, p. 236; Joseph Gutmann,
"Jewish Participation in the Visual Arts of
Eighteenth and Nineteenth Century America,"
American Jewish Archives, XV, I, p. 47.
Exhibited: *Cincinnati Industrial Exposition*,
1882, No. 459.
Gift of Joseph W. Wayne.

1881.57
MERSMAN, Ferdinand (1852-?), BUST OF A GIRL,
1881. Terra cotta, height 16¾ (42.5), width 9¹⁄₁₆ (23.0),
depth 7½ (19.0).
Mersman was engaged by the Women's Art
Museum Association of Cincinnati around 1879 to
teach classes in modeling. He also worked
occasionally for Rookwood Pottery.
Gift of the Women's Art Museum Association.

1905.196
NIEHAUS, Charles Henry (1855-1935), PORTRAIT OF
ROBERT BLUM, Cincinnati. Bronze, height 20⁷⁄₁₆ (51.9),
width 13²⁹⁄₃₂ (35.3), depth 10⁵⁄₁₆ (26.2).
Inscribed: lower left on shoulder, "C.H. Niehaus sc.";
on right shoulder, "cast by Aubry Bros. Co. N.Y.";
on marble base, "Robert F. Blum 1858-1903,
C.H.Niehaus, sculptor."
Niehaus, born in Cincinnati, began his career at the
McMicken School of Design, going on from there
to Europe in 1877.
Published: *Cincinnati Museum Review of the
Collections*, 1924, fig. 61.

Exhibited: *American Masters of Sculpture*, Herron
Museum of Art, Indianapolis, 1965, No. 13, illus-
trated.
Gift of Henrietta Haller.

1923.770
NIEHAUS, Charles Henry (1855-1935), PORTRAIT
OF DANIEL W. HOLMES, Cincinnati. Marble, height
24 (61.0), width 12⅞ (32.8), depth 10⁷⁄₃₂ (23.4).
Gift of Mrs. Daniel W. Holmes.

1962.68
BARNHORN, Clement J. (1857-1935), MAENADS,
Cincinnati, 1901. Plaster, height 28½ (72.4), width
84⁹⁄₁₆ (214.8), max. depth 7⅞ (20.0).
Inscribed: lower right, "Clement J. Barnhorn,"
date blurred.
Plaster version of bronze in Queen City Club,
Cincinnati.
Exhibited: *Special Exhibition of Sculpture by C. J.
Barnhorn of Cincinnati*, Cincinnati Art Museum,
Mar.-Apr. 1914, No. 17; *Retrospective Exhibition of
Sculpture by Clement J. Barnhorn*, Cincinnati Art
Museum, Jan.-Feb. 1934, No. 12.
Gift of Henry Gest.

1910.1
BARNHORN, Clement J. (1857-1935), PORTRAIT OF
FRANK DUVENECK, Cincinnati, 1908. Bronze, height
27⁷⁄₁₆ (67.1), width 20¾ (52.6), depth 11⁷⁄₁₆ (29.1).
Inscribed: back, "Clement J. Barnhorn—1908."
Published: *Cincinnati Museum Review of the
Collections*, 1924, fig. 19.
Exhibited: *Special Exhibition of Sculpture by C. J.
Barnhorn of Cincinnati*, Cincinnati Art Museum,
Mar.-Apr. 1914, No. 35.
Gift of Frank Duveneck.

1921.490
BARNHORN, Clement J. (1857-1935), ALMA MATER,
Cincinnati, 1910-12. Plaster, height 65¹⁵⁄₁₆ (167.5),
width 22¹³⁄₁₆ (58.0), depth 16⅜ (41.6).
Inscribed: right side of base, "Clement J. Barnhorn."
Original plaster version of figure on the portal of
the Cathedral Basilica of the Assumption in
Covington, Ky., and intended by Barnhorn as a
memorial to his parents.
Exhibited: *Special Exhibition of Sculpture by C. J.

1921.490

Barnhorn of Cincinnati, Cincinnati Art Museum,
Mar.-Apr. 1914, No. 41 or 43; *Retrospective
Exhibition of Sculpture by Clement J. Barnhorn,*
Cincinnati Art Museum, Jan-Feb. 1934, No. 22.
Gift of the artist.

X1964.19
BARNHORN, Clement J. (1857-1935), MADONNA,
1913. Plaster, height 12⁷⁄₁₆ (31.5), width 6⁹⁄₁₆ (16.6),
depth 3⅞ (9.9).
Penciled on back: "Original master sketch model
for Barnhorn family monument St. John's Cemetery
St. Bernard 1913 in bronze and granite by
Clement J. Barnhorn."
Bequest of the artist.

1958.477
BARNHORN, Clement J. (1857-1935), SAN
DOMINGO INDIAN DANCING, 1918. Bronze, height
13¹¹⁄₁₆ (34.7), width 4⁹⁄₃₂ (10.9), depth 4³⁄₁₆ (10.6).
Inscribed: left side of base, "19 Ⓒ 18 C. J.
BARNHORN TAOS, N. MEX."; back of base,
"ROMAN BRONZE WORKS N-Y-."
Exhibited: *Retrospective Exhibition of Sculpture by
Clement J. Barnhorn,* Cincinnati Art Museum,
Jan.-Feb. 1934, No. 37.
Collections: Mary Hanna, Cincinnati, 1934.
Gift of John B. Hollister.

1911.1344
BLUM, Robert Frederick (1857-1903), DANCING
FIGURE. Plaster, height 15¹⁄₁₆ (38.2), width 3⅞ (9.9),
depth 3⅞ (9.9).
Inscribed: front of base, "BLUM."
Blum, born in Cincinnati and a pupil of the
McMicken School of Design, was primarily a painter,
but several of these small figures, made as studies for
paintings, were found in his studio after his death.
Published: *Retrospective Exhibition of Robert Blum,*
Cincinnati Art Museum, Apr. 1-May 7, 1966, No. 166.
Gift of Augustus Lukeman.

1921.250
BLUM, Robert Frederick (1857-1903), RECLINING
FIGURES. Plaster, height 9³⁄₁₆ (23.4), width 17⅛ (43.5),
depth 4⅛ (10.5).
Not signed, but lower right corner is broken off
and may have borne signature. Plaster model for

bronze (1905.142). Made as a study for a painting of figures symbolizing Summer.
Gift of William J. Baer.

1905.142
BLUM, Robert Frederick (1857-1903), RECLINING FIGURES. Bronze relief, height 9⅛ (23.1), width 16⅞ (42.8), depth 4 (10.2)
Inscribed: lower right, "AUBRY BROS CO. FOUNDERS, N-Y-"; upper right, "R. Blum."
This is a bronze cast from a plaster model (1921.250) for figures in his murals for Mendelsohn Hall, New York City.
Published: *Retrospective Exhibition of Robert Blum*, Cincinnati Art Museum, Apr. 1-May 7, 1966, No. 164.

1920.395
ELWELL, Francis Edwin (1858-1922), PORTRAIT OF JAMES E. MOONEY. Marble, height with base 29⅛ (74.0), width 17¼ (43.8), depth 11 (27.9).
Gift of Charles L. Harrison.

1954.417
MEYENBERG, John C. (1860-1936), BEHREN'S DAUGHTER, Cincinnati. Plaster, height 14¹³⁄₃₂ (36.6), width 11⅝ (29.4), depth 8³⁄₁₆ (20.8).
Inscribed: left side of base, "J. C. MEYENBERG SCULPT."
Meyenberg is reported to have done a portrait of Ben Pittman for the Cincinnati Public Library and decorative panels for other buildings in the area. He was also associated with Rookwood Pottery.
Gift of Harry Mulvey.

1916.299
HARVEY, Eli (1860-1957), RECUMBENT GREYHOUND. Bronze, height 10¹¹⁄₁₆ (27.1), width 6¹³⁄₁₆ (17.3), depth 23⅞ (60.6).
Inscribed: right side of base, "Eli.Harvey.fecit.1912."; back of base, "B.ZOPPO.FOUNDRIES.N.Y.C.";
left side of base, "Copyright.1912.by.Eli.Harvey."
Harvey studied at the Art Academy of Cincinnati under Rebisso ca. 1884.
Purchased through a fund given by M. M. White.

1952.115
REMINGTON, Frederick, (1861-1909), THE BRONCO BUSTER. Bronze, height 22⁹⁄₁₆ (57.2), width at base 15⅜ (39.1), depth at base 7⅜ (18.7).

Inscribed: top of base, "Copyright by Frederick Remington"; "ROMAN BRONZE WORKS NEW YORK"; under side of base, "No. 163."
Exhibited: *The Wild West*, Louisville Public Library, Junior Art Gallery, June 22-July 29, 1953.
Gift of Mrs. Benjamin Tate.

1957.221
VALENTIEN, Anna Marie (1862-1947), PORTRAIT OF MRS. MATT DALY, Cincinnati, 1893. Plaster, height 24½ (62.2), width 15³⁄₁₆ (38.6), depth 9¹³⁄₁₆ (24.8).
Inscribed: right side of base, "A.M. Valentien 1893."
Anna Valentien was primarily a decorator for Rookwood Pottery.
Gift of H. M. Everson.

1919.453
GRAFLY, Charles (1862-1929), PORTRAIT OF FRANK DUVENECK, 1915. Bronze, height 27⅛ (68.9), width 14⅛ (35.9), depth 11½ (29.2).
Inscribed: "Charles Grafly"; left side "Roman Bronze Works, N-Y"; back, "FRANK DUVENECK MADE AT FOLLY COVE-CAPE ANN-MASSACHUSETTS-AUGUST-1915."
Exhibited: *American Masters of Sculpture*, Herron Museum of Art, Indianapolis, 1965, No. 18, illustrated.

1959.165
MacMONNIES, Frederick (1863-1937), BACCHANTE AND CHILD, 1893. Bronze, height 16¹⁵⁄₃₂ (41.8), width 4⅞ (12.4), depth 3¹¹⁄₁₆ (9.3),
Inscribed: base, "F. MacMonnies 1893 H. ROUARD FONDEUR."
Large version in Metropolitan Museum of Art, New York, completed in 1894.
Published: *Yearbook*, Grand Central Art Galleries, 1957, illustrated p. 43, No. 45; Craven, *Sculpture in America*, 1968, fig. 12.3.
Gift of Mrs. Henry Matson Waite.

1952.65
BORGLUM, John Gutzon (1867-1941), FIGURE OF A WOMAN. Marble, height 24³¹⁄₃₂ (63.4), width 7²⁹⁄₃₂ (20.1), depth 8¹⁵⁄₁₆ (22.6).
Published: Craven, *Sculpture in America*, 1968, p. 489.
Exhibited: *American Masters of Sculpture*, Herron Museum of Art, Indianapolis, 1965, No. 28, illustrated.
Gift of the Estate of Eda Kuhn Loeb.

1898.256
BORGLUM, Solon H. (1868-1922), Winter (Little Horse in the Wind). Bronze, height $10\frac{7}{16}$ (26.5), width $3\frac{7}{8}$ (9.8), depth $13\frac{5}{32}$ (33.4).
Inscribed: front of base, "Solon Borglum."
This work was cast from the model bought by the Museum from the artist who studied at the Cincinnati Art Academy 1895-97 under Louis T. Rebisso.
Published: *Catalog of Oil Paintings and Sculpture in the Art Museum,* Cincinnati, 1904, 1905, S.21; Craven, *Sculpture in America,* 1968, p. 525.
Gift of W. W. Taylor, M. E. Ingalls, D. H. Holmes, Alexander McDonald, L. B. Harrison, J. G. Schmidlapp.

1904.18
VONNOH, Bessie Potter (1872-1955), A Study (seated woman). Bronze, height $7\frac{7}{8}$ (20.0), width $5\frac{5}{8}$ (14.2), depth $6\frac{9}{16}$ (16.6).
Inscribed: left side at bottom, "Bessie Potter Vonnoh" (date indecipherable); on back at bottom, "Roman Bronze Works N.Y."

1904.19
VONNOH, Bessie Potter (1872-1954), Hester. Bronze, height $9\frac{15}{16}$ (25.3), width $7\frac{5}{8}$ (19.3), depth $4\frac{7}{16}$ (10.2).
Inscribed: right side of base, "Bessie Potter Vonnoh 1901"; left side of base, "Roman Bronze Works N.Y."
Published: Craven, *Sculpture in America,* 1968, p. 502.

1912.1
LONGMAN, Evelyn Beatrice (Mrs. Nathaniel Horton Batchelder) (1874-1954), Bust of J. G. Schmidlapp, early XX c. Bronze, height $24\frac{7}{16}$ (62.0), width $22\frac{3}{4}$ (58.3), depth $15\frac{3}{16}$ (38.5).
Gift of the artist.

1957.223
PHILBIN, Clara (1875-1944), Girl Reading, Cincinnati, 1909. Plaster, height 24 (61.0), width (of book) $21\frac{1}{4}$ (54.0), depth $16\frac{1}{8}$ (41.5).
Gift of Booth Shepard.

1957.224
PHILBIN, Clara (1875-1944), Portrait Bust of a Child, Cincinnati. Plaster, height $26\frac{9}{16}$ (67.5), width $16\frac{7}{8}$ (43.0), depth $10\frac{1}{4}$ (26.0).
Gift of Booth Shepard.

1910.565
ALEXANDER, Mary (Mrs. W. J. R.) (1875-1963), Vincent Nowottny Memorial Tablet, Cincinnati, 1910. Bronze, height $30\frac{1}{4}$ (76.8), width $19\frac{1}{8}$ (48.5), depth $2\frac{15}{16}$ (7.5).
Gift of Class of Vincent Nowottny.

1941.258
HUNTINGTON, Anna Vaughn Hyatt (b. 1876), Zebra and Foal, 1939. Aluminum, height $20\frac{3}{8}$ (51.7), width $26\frac{5}{8}$ (67.6), depth $10\frac{15}{16}$ (27.8).
Inscribed: side of base, "Lève-toi Mama j'ai faim"; back of base, "Anna Hyatt Huntington 1939 C"; right side of base, "ROMAN BRONZE WORKS, N.Y."
Gift of the artist.

1956.235
FRISHMUTH, Harriet Whiting (b. 1880), Joy of Water, 1912. Bronze, height $61\frac{7}{16}$ (156.0), width $13\frac{13}{16}$ (35.0), depth $12\frac{3}{4}$ (32.5).
Inscribed: base, "Harriet W. Frishmuth SC 1912."
Gift of E. B. Stanley.

1969.518
DAVIDSON, Jo (1883-1952), Head of L. R. Culver as a Child, Paris, 1907-8. Plaster, height $13\frac{1}{8}$ (33.3), width 10 (25.4), depth $6\frac{3}{4}$ (17.2).
This head is all that survives of a complete figure.
Gift of Mr. and Mrs. Laurence R. Culver.

1916.4
MANSHIP, Paul (1885-1966), Little Brother, 1912. Bronze, height $12\frac{5}{8}$ (32.0), width of base $4\frac{11}{16}$ (11.9), depth of base $7\frac{3}{8}$ (18.8).
Inscribed: top of base, "PAUL MANSHIP ROMA C 1912"; back of base, "ROMAN BRONZE WORKS N-Y-"

1916.5
MANSHIP, Paul (1885-1966), Lyric Muse, 1912. Bronze, height $11\frac{3}{4}$ (29.8), width of base $6\frac{15}{16}$ (17.6), depth $5\frac{9}{16}$ (14.2).
Inscribed: top of base, "PAUL MANSHIP C ROME 1912"; right side of base, "ROMAN BRONZE WORKS N-Y-"

1918.34
FRANCISCI, Anthony de (b. 1887), Bayadere. Bronze, height $19\frac{7}{8}$ (50.5), width 12 (30.0), depth $11\frac{1}{32}$ (28.0).
Exhibited: *Twenty-Fifth Exhibition of American Art,* Cincinnati Art Museum, Summer 1918.

1916.4

1937.626
HASWELL, Ernest Bruce (1887-1965), BUST OF
FREDERICK HERMAN ALMS, Cincinnati. Marble, height
19⁷⁄₁₆ (49.3), width 20⅞ (53.0), depth 13⅛ (32.4).
Gift of the Alms Estate.

1937.625
HASWELL, Ernest Bruce (1887-1965), BUST OF
MRS. ELEANORA C. UNZICKER ALMS, Cincinnati.
Marble, height 19⁵⁄₁₆ (49.1), width 20¼ (51.5),
depth 10⅝ (27.0).
Gift of the Alms Estate.

1951.189
LIPCHITZ, Jacques (b. 1891), PEGASUS, 1944.
Bronze, height 15½ (39.4), width 20⁹⁄₁₆ (52.3),
depth 7⅛ (18.1).
Related to "Birth of the Muses," an overmantel in
the guest house of John D. Rockefeller III, New York.
Published: *College Art Journal,* Summer 1954, cover;
Sculpture in Europe Today, University of California
Press, 1955, No. 91; *Cincinnati Art Museum Guide,*
1956, p. 17.
Exhibited: University of Kentucky, Lexington, Ky.,
Nov. 19, 1949-Jan. 20, 1950; *Jacques Lipchitz, An
Exhibition of His Sculpture and Drawings 1914-1950,*
Portland Art Museum, San Francisco Museum of Art,
Cincinnati Art Museum, 1950-51, No. 15.
Gift of the Cincinnati Modern Art Society.

1942.83
ABEL, Louise (b. 1894), YOUNG HIMALAYAN
MOUNTAIN GOAT, 1942. Terra cotta, height 8⅝
(21.8), width 2¾ (7.0), depth 7³⁄₃₂ (18.0).
Inscribed: "Louise Abel."
A student at the Art Academy of Cincinnati under
Barnhorn ca. 1909, she was active in Cincinnati
intermittently until about 1955.
Exhibited: *Exhibition of Contemporary Ceramics of
the Western Hemisphere,* April 3-26, 1942, No. 4;
Columbus Gallery of Fine Arts, Ohio, July 10-Aug. 2,
1953; *Contemporary Ohio Ceramics Exhibition,*
Akron Art Institute, Ohio, Sept. 29-Oct. 25, 1953.

1938.10571 and 1938.10605
FLANNAGAN, John B. (1895-1942), HEAD OF A
WOMAN, 1932 (two examples). Cast cement, each
height 10¼ (26.6), width 6¹¹⁄₁₆ (17.0), depth 5¾ (14.6).
Exhibited: *What in the World?* University Museum,
TV program, University of Pennsylvania,
Philadelphia, Oct. 10, 1954.

1913.259
JEHU, John M. (XIX-XX c.), THE PRINCESS AND THE
FROG. Bronze, height 10⅝ (27.0), width 3 (7.7),
diameter of base 3¹⁄₁₆ (7.8).
Inscribed: left side of base, "JEHU"; back of base,
"cast by Gifford (?) Newark, N.J."
Jehu studied at the Art Academy of Cincinnati
1898-1903.
Exhibited: *Twentieth Annual Exhibition of Amer-
ican Art,* Cincinnati Art Museum, Summer 1913.

1951.189

1965.516

1944.107
HAUPT, Charlotte (b. 1898), REFUGEE MOTHER AND CHILD, Cincinnati. Stone, height 13¹⁵⁄₁₆ (35.5), width 9⁷⁄₁₆ (24.0); depth 5½ (14.0).
A student at the University of Cincinnati and under Barnhorn at the Art Academy of Cincinnati, she was active in Cincinnati until the 1950's.
Gift of Mrs. Frederick A. Geier.

1965.516
CALDER, Alexander (b. 1898), TWENTY LEAVES AND AN APPLE, 1946. Sheet metal and piano wire painted black except for one disk painted red, height ca. 7' (213.5), width 14' (427.0).
Commissioned for the lobby of the Terrace Plaza Hotel, Cincinnati, Ohio, where it hung until 1965.
Published: H. H. Arnason, *Calder*, 1966, D. Van Nostrand, Inc., Princeton, N.J., pp. 76, 83, 166; *Cincinnati Art Museum Bulletin*, Jan. 1968, p. 47, illustrated.
Gift of Thomas Emery's Sons, Inc.

1938.10606
SCARAVAGLIONE, Concetta (b. 1900), SEATED WOMAN WITH A GUITAR, New York City, Cast stone, height 12³⁄₃₂ (30.7), width at base 3¹³⁄₁₆ (9.7), depth at base 5¹³⁄₁₆ (14.7).
Inscribed: left side of base, "CONCETTA SCARAVAGLIONE C R.G.I."; back of base, "Robinson Galleries Inc. New York City."

1968.3
SINAIKO, Arlie (b. 1902), VAGUE VERTICALE. Bronze, height 30¾ (78.3), width 8½ (21.5), depth 4¼ (10.8).
Gift of Mrs. Arlie Sinaiko.

1952.108
CALLERY, Mary (b. 1903), THE CURVE, 1947. Bronze, height 21²¹⁄₃₂ (55.0), width 7⅛ (18.1), depth 28¼ (71.8).
Inscribed: "MC."
Published: Curt Valentin & Co., *In Memory of Curt*

Valentin, Oct. 5-30, 1954, No. 4, illustrated; Philip R. Adams, *Mary Callery Sculpture*, Wittenborn, New York, 1961, p. 31.
Gift of the Cincinnati Modern Art Society.

1961.220
CALLERY, Mary (b. 1903), COMPOSITION No. 12, 1960. Mixed metals, height 10¾ (27.3), width 13²⁵⁄₃₂ (35.0), depth 6⁹⁄₃₂ (16.0).
Published: Philip R. Adams, *Mary Callery Sculpture*, Wittenborn, New York, 1961, p. 129.
Gift of the artist.

1929.376
THEIS, Gladys Huling (Mrs. Charles V.) (b. 1903), PORTRAIT OF CLEMENT J. BARNHORN, 1928-29. Bronze, height 20⅜ (52.4), width 10¹⁄₁₆ (25.5), depth 9⁹⁄₃₂ (23.1).

Inscribed: front of base, "CLEMENT JOHN BARNHORN/GLADYS HULING THEIS SC. 1929"; back, "C. J. Barnhorn by G. Huling Theis 1928."
Exhibited: *Exhibition of Students' Work*, Cincinnati Art Academy, 1929.
Gift of Harry Fowler Woods.

1954.176
SMITH, David (1906-1965), ENTRANCE, 1951. Steel, height 31¹³⁄₁₆ (80.8), width 32⅜ (82.2), depth 10⅛ (25.6).
Exhibited: *David Smith, Sculpture, Drawings, Graphics*, Contemporary Arts Center, Cincinnati Art Museum, May 19-June 13, 1954, No. 5; *David Smith, A Retrospective Exhibition*, Fogg Art Museum, 1966, No. 200, p. 72.
Gift of the Cincinnati Modern Art Society.

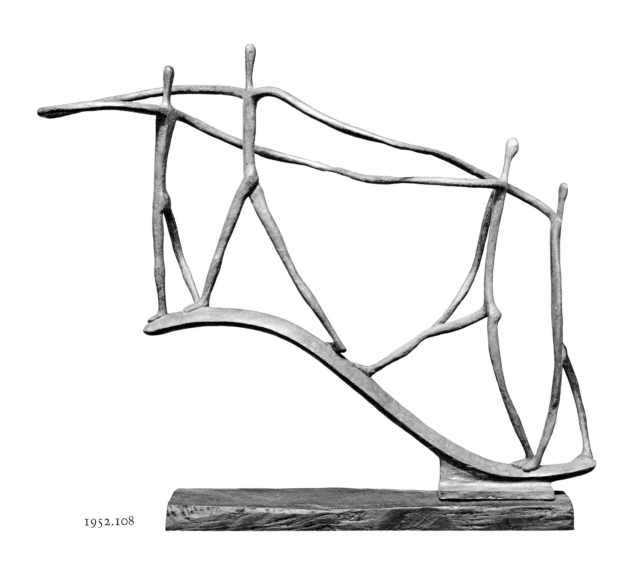

1952.108

1953.55
BARELA, Patrocinio (b. 1908), FATHER AND CHILD.
Red cedar, height 25 (63.6), width 13⅛ (33.3),
depth 6¹⁵⁄₁₆ (17.6).
Inscribed: bottom of right foot, "Pat.B."
Gift of Mrs. Howard Wurlitzer.

1953.56
BARELA, Patrocinio (b. 1908), MINUTE MAN. Red
cedar, height 9⁹⁄₁₆ (24.3), width 4¹¹⁄₁₆ (11.9),
depth 3¹¹⁄₁₆ (9.3).
Inscribed: back, "Pat.B."
Gift of Mrs. Howard Wurlitzer.

1953.51
BARELA, Patrocinio (b. 1908), FLIGHT INTO EGYPT.
Red cedar, height 15⅜ (39.0), width 12³⁄₁₆ (31.0),
depth 4¹³⁄₁₆ (12.3).
Inscribed: bottom of base, "Pat.B."
Gift of Mrs. Howard Wurlitzer.

1953.53
BARELA, Patrocinio (b. 1908), PATERNITY. Red cedar,
height 14⁹⁄₁₆ (37.1), width 5⅜ (13.6), depth 3¹¹⁄₁₆ (9.3).
Inscribed: bottom, "Pat.B."
Gift of Mrs. Howard Wurlitzer.

1953.52
BARELA, Patrocinio (b. 1908), SACRED THOUGHT.
Red cedar, height 13¹⁄₁₆ (33.2), width 3⁷⁄₁₆ (8.8),
depth 3⅛ (7.9).
Inscribed: bottom of base "Pat.B."
Gift of Mrs. Howard Wurlitzer.

1953.54
BARELA, Patrocinio, (b. 1908), FAMILY LOVE. Red
cedar, height 10¾ (27.3), width 6¾ (17.2),
depth 4¹⁵⁄₁₆ (12.5).
Inscribed: bottom, "Pat.B."
Gift of Mrs. Howard Wurlitzer.

1949.35
CUTLER, Charles Gordon (b. 1914), BIRTH OF A
SNAKE, 1941. Grano-diorite, height 9¼ (23.5), width
16⅜ (41.5), depth 11¼ (28.6).
Published: "Cincinnati Art Museum News,"
Magazine of Art, May 1949, p. iii; *Art Digest*, Aug.
1, 1950, p. 11; *The Sculpture of Charles Cutler*,
Cincinnati Art Museum, Jan. 1969, No. 14, cover.

Exhibited: *Kurt Roesch, Charles Cutler*, Buchholz
Gallery, New York, Oct. 29-Nov. 16, 1946, No. 17;
Crawford, Cutler, Cincinnati Art Museum, Feb.
16-Mar. 15, 1949, No. 36; Skowhegan School of
Painting and Sculpture, Nov. 9-20, 1954; *The
Sculpture of Charles Cutler*, Cincinnati, 1969, No. 14.
Gift of Charles W. Adler.

1968.524
ZOGBAUM, Wilfred (1915-1965), GREAT CAPTAIN
ROCKS, 1960. Painted steel and stone, height 59
(149.8), width 48¼ (122.6), depth 19¼ (48.9).
Inscribed: "Zogbaum."
Exhibited: *Contemporary American Sculpture*,
Whitney Museum, New York, Oct. 1960;
International Sculpture Exhibition, Vanderbilt
University, 1961.
The Edwin and Virginia Irwin Memorial

1968.524

1968.523
HASSELLE, Robert (b. 1942), SPIRIT OF PLACE (FOR
WILLIAM CARLOS WILLIAMS), 1966. Bronze, height 32½
(82.5), width 18¼ (46.5), depth 19¼ (49).
Published: *The Cincinnati Biennial Awards
Exhibition.* Cincinnati Art Museum, Nov. 20, 1968-
Jan. 1, 1969, No. 59.
The Edwin and Virginia Irwin Memorial

1954.176

1955.794
FIGUREHEAD, XIX c. Wood painted, height
66 (167.7), width 25 (63.5).
Published: Pauline Pinckney, *American Figureheads
and Their Carvers*, New York, 1940, pl. 78 and p. 173.
Draped figure of a man, ¾ length, standing with
head up and sword held in two hands, a type
known as the "Scottish Gael."
Gift of Mr. and Mrs. Carl J. Rauh

1884.369
GREYHOUND, XIX c.
Marble, height 14½ (36.8), width 12½ (31.8),
depth 24½ (62.2).
Gift of Reuben R. Springer.

1958.446
BIRD, Pennsylvania German, XIX c. Wood,
height 4 (10.1), width 1⅛ (2.8), depth 3½ (8.8).
Carol R. Guggenheim Memorial Fund.

1958.444
DECOY DUCK, XIX c. Wood painted, height
9 (22.8), width 5⅛ (12.9), depth 17⅛ (43.5).
Inscribed: "G. Wood."
Carol R. Guggenheim Memorial Fund.

1958.445
DECOY GOOSE HEAD, XIX c. Wood,
painted, height 13⁹⁄₁₆ (34.5), width 6⅞ (17.5),
depth 6⅛ (15.6).
Carol R. Guggenheim Memorial Fund.

1958.447 a and b
DECOY SNIPES, XIX c. Wood, a) height
6¹³⁄₁₆ (17.2), width 2¾ (6.9) depth 12½
(31.6); b) height 5⁹⁄₁₆ (14.2), width 2⅜ (6.0),
depth 12⅞ (32.7).
Carol R. Guggenheim Memorial Fund.

1958.630
BIRD, XIX c. Wood, height 4¼ (10.9), width
1¹⁵⁄₁₆ (4.9), depth 5¼ (13.2).
Carol R. Guggenheim Memorial Fund.

1958.632
DECOY SHORE BIRD, XIX c. Wood, height
7¹⁄₁₆ (18.0), width 1¼ (3.2), depth 7½ (19.1).
Carol R. Guggenheim Memorial Fund.

1958.447 a and b

1958.450
EAGLE, Bellamy type, XIX c. Wood, height 9³⁄₁₆
(23.4), width 22³⁄₁₆ (56.4), depth 6¹⁄₁₆ (15.4).
Carol R. Guggenheim Memorial Fund.

1958.429
HEAD OF A MAN (thought to be a portrait of
a church elder), New England, XIX c. Wood,
height 6⅞ (17.4), width 2⅛ (5.4), depth 3½ (8.9).
Gift of Mrs. Albert Strauss in memory of
Carol R. Guggenheim.

American Indian

1906.130
TOTEM POLE, Haida tribe, Northwest Coast,
XIX c. Black slate, height 19 (48.3), width of base
3¹⁵⁄₁₆ (10.0), of top 1⅞ (4.8), depth of base 3⅜ (8.5),
of top 1½ (3.7).
Gift of W. N. King.

1936.556
TOTEM POLE, Haida tribe, Northwest Coast,
XIX c. Black slate, height 11⅛ (28.2), width of base
2⅞ (7.8), of top 1⅜ (3.5), depth of base 1⁵⁄₁₆ (6.0),
of top ⅞ (2.3).
Bequest of Charlotte H. Mackenzie.

X1968.3
TOTEM POLE, Haida tribe, Northwest Coast,
XIX c. Black slate, height 13½ (34.3), width of base
2¹⁵⁄₁₆ (7.5), of top 1³⁄₁₆ (3.0), depth of base 2⁷⁄₁₆ (6.2),
of top 1 (2.5).
Anonymous gift.

1923.843
CARVED PLANK, Alaska, early XIX c. Painted
wood, height 10⅜ (26.4), width 33⅜ (84.4),
depth ⅝ (1.6).
Collections: Dr. B. K. Wilbur, Sitka, Alaska.
Gift of Mrs. William H. Taylor.

X1965.15
VESSEL WITH DUCK'S HEAD, Tlingit tribe,
Northwest Coast, XIX c. Mountain-sheep horn,
height 4⅞ (12.4), width 5½ (14.0), depth 7¹⁄₁₆ (18.0).
Anonymous gift.

1888.512
BIRD STONE, said to have been found near
Cincinnati, Ohio, Moundbuilder culture. Stone,
height 2 (5.0), width 1¼ (3.0), depth 5⅞ (14.9).
Gift of Joseph Cox.

X1965.15

1888.512

1939.140

1938.5124

1938.5124
MASK, said to have been found in the Tennessee River valley, Moundbuilder culture. Stone, height 8½ (21.5), width 6¾ (17.0), depth 3⁷⁄₁₆ (8.7).
Published: Gustav G. Carlson, "The American Indian Collection," *Bulletin of the Cincinnati Art Museum*, x, 1, Jan. 1939, p. 7, illustrated p. 8; Cottie Burland, *North American Indian Mythology*, Paul Hamlyn, London, 1966, p. 126.
Anonymous gift.

1939.140
ENGRAVED TABLET, Waverly, Ohio, Hopewell culture. Stone, height 3⅜ (8.6), width 2⁹⁄₁₆ (6.6), depth ⁵⁄₁₆ (0.9).
Published: Gustav G. Carlson, "The American Indian Collection," *Bulletin of the Cincinnati Art Museum*, x, 1, Jan. 1939, p. 7.
Gift of Mrs. William L. Galt

1887.20607
MASK, said to have been found in the Tennessee River valley, Moundbuilder culture. Shell, height 7¹⁵⁄₁₆ (20.2), width 6¹³⁄₁₆ (15.7), depth 2³⁄₁₆ (5.5).
Published: *Cincinnati Art Museum* Guide, 1956, p. 36.
Gift of Thomas Cleneay.

1887.20610
MASK, said to have been found in a mound in Tennessee, Moundbuilder culture. Shell, height 8 (20.2), width 7 (17.7), depth 2⅜ (6.0).
Exhibited: *What in the World?*, TV program, University Museum, University of Pennsylvania, Oct. 10, 1963.
Gift of Thomas Cleneay.

1961.270
SEATED FEMALE FIGURE, Nicaragua, Pacific Coast, Nicoya polychrome, 600-1200 A.D. Pottery, height 6¹⁵⁄₁₆ (17.6), width 4¹⁹⁄₃₂ (11.7), depth 3⅜ (8.6).
Gift of Dr. and Mrs. Martin B. Macht.

1887.20607

African

1964.157
ANTELOPE AND YOUNG, Bambara, Mali.
Wood, height 26⅜ (67.0), width 3 (7.5),
depth 10¼ (26.0).
A fertility symbol, originally part of a dance
headdress.
Gift of Mary Mills Ford, Olive Lloyd Mills and
Marcia Mills Bogart in memory of
Edward Lloyd Mills.

1956.213
FIGURE OF A MAN, Belgian Congo, Basonga
Tribe. Wood, height 9⅜ (23.8), width 1¾ (4.4),
depth 1¹³⁄₁₆ (4.6).
Gift of Raymond Weilgus per Julius Carlebach.

1956.209
WEIGHT FOR GOLD DUST IN THE FORM
OF A BELT, Ashanti, XIX c. Bronze, height 1³⁄₁₆
(3.0), width 1½ (3.9), depth ¹³⁄₁₆ (2.1).
Gift of Raymond Wielgus per Julius Carlebach.

1956.210
WEIGHT FOR GOLD DUST IN THE FORM
OF A SCORPION, Ashanti, XIX c. Bronze, height
1¹⁄₁₆ (2.7), width 1⁷⁄₁₆ (3.6), depth 2¾ (7.0).
Gift of Raymond Wielgus per Julius Carlebach.

1956.447
FEMALE FIGURE, Baoulé, Ivory Coast, XIX c.
Wood, height 9¹⁵⁄₁₆ (25.3), width 1½ (3.3),
depth 1¹³⁄₁₆ (4.6).
Collections: Dr. and Mrs. Alfred B. Lippert (on loan
to the Cincinnati Art Museum 1904-1956).
Gift of Karl Morgan Lippert.

1890.1545
WOMAN HOLDING CALABASH RATTLES,
Balumbo, Congo. Wood, inlaid glass eyes, applied
wire and string, height 16⅝ (42.3), width
5¹³⁄₁₆ (14.8), depth 5 (12.7).
Published: Erwin Ottomar Christensen, *Primitive
Art*, Crowell, New York, 1955, p. 49, fig. 46;
Cincinnati Art Museum Guide, 1956, p. 36; Warren
M. Robbins, *African Art in American Collections*,
Praeger, New York, 1966, pl. 244.

1964.157

Exhibited: *African Exhibition*, Taft Museum,
Cincinnati, March 1946; *The African Image*, Toledo
Museum of Art, Feb. 1959, No. 127, illustrated p. 25.
Collections: Carl Steckelmann, Columbus, Ind.;
Henry Brockmann, Columbus, Ind., 1889-1890.
The Steckelmann collection was purchased for the
Museum by special subscription from the following:
Alexander McDonald, L. B. Harrison, M. E. Ingalls,
J. Schmidlapp, W. P. Anderson, Leon Van Loo,
W. W. Seely, Julius Dexter, Herman Goepper,
R. H. Galbraith, and A. T. Goshorn, Director.

1890.1528
CEREMONIAL STAFF, Congo. Wood, height 17
(43.2), width 1⁹⁄₁₆ (3.9), depth 1¼ (3.2).
Exhibited: *African Exhibition*, Taft Museum,
Cincinnati, March 1946.
Collections: Carl Steckelmann, Columbus, Ind.;
Henry Brockmann, Columbus, Ind., 1889-1890.
Gift by special subscription: see 1890.1545.

1890.1545

1890.848
MASK, Ogowe River, Gabun. Painted wood, height
10⅝ (27.0), width 6⁹⁄₁₆ (16.7), depth 3⅜ (8.6).
Collections: Carl Steckelmann, Columbus, Ind.;
Henry Brockmann, Columbus, Ind., 1889-1890.
Gift by special subscription: see 1890.1545.

1890.849
MASK, Ogowe River, Gabun. Painted wood, height
9¹⁵⁄₁₆ (25.3), width 5¹³⁄₁₆ (4.7), depth 3¹³⁄₁₆ (9.6).
Exhibited: *African Exhibition,* Taft Museum,
Cincinnati, March 1946.
Collections: Carl Steckelmann, Columbus, Ind.;
Henry Brockmann, Columbus, Ind., 1889-1890.
Gift by special subscription: see 1890.1545.

1890.1516
HAMMOCK PIN, Mendi, Sierra Leone, XIX c.
Wood, height 14⅝ (37.1), width 1⁹⁄₁₆ (3.9),
depth 1½ (3.8).
Collections: Carl Steckelmann, Columbus, Ind.;
Henry Brockmann, Columbus, Ind., 1889-1890.
Gift by special subscription: see 1890.1545.

1890.1533
WAR CLUB, Congo, XIX c. Wood, height 30¼
(76.8), diameter of shaft ⅞ (2.2), diameter of carved
bands 1¾ (4.4).
Collections: Carl Steckelmann, Columbus, Ind.;
Henry Brockmann, Columbus, Ind., 1889-1890.
Gift by special subscription: see 1890.1545.

Abbreviations

Dimensions are given in inches followed by centimeters in parentheses. Where human or animal figures were concerned, *width* was taken in a shoulder-to-shoulder direction and *depth* was taken at right angles to width, in the direction chest-to-back. Where no donor is named, Museum purchase is implied.

Abbreviations for frequently cited references are listed below alphabetically with the complete reference following the colon.

Ackerman, *Guide to the Exhibition of Persian Art*, 1940 : Phyllis Ackerman, *Guide to the Exhibition of Persian Art*, Iranian Institute, New York, 1940

Adams, *Cincinnati Art Museum Bulletin*, Feb. 1951: Philip R. Adams, "Sculpture of the Middle East," *Cincinnati Art Museum Bulletin*, I, 3, Feb. 1951

Adams, *Cincinnati Art Museum Bulletin*, Summer, 1951: Philip R. Adams, "Sculpture of the Far East," *Cincinnati Art Museum Bulletin*, I, 5-6, Summer 1951

Adams, *Cincinnati Art Museum Bulletin*, Mar. 1953: Philip R. Adams, "Five Buddhist Sculptures," *Cincinnati Art Museum Bulletin*, III, 2, Mar. 1953

Ancient Civilizations, Cincinnati, 1961 : *Ancient Civilizations/Egypt, Greece, Rome*, Cincinnati Art Museum, 1961

Archives of Chinese Art : *Archives of the Chinese Art Society in America*

Cincinnati Museum Review, 1924 : *Cincinnati Museum Review of the Collections Prepared to Aid Students in Using Them as a Key to the History and Appreciation of Art*, 1924

Craven, *Sculpture in America*, 1968 : Wayne Craven, *Sculpture in America*, Thomas Y. Crowell, New York, 1968

Culican, *Medes and Persians*, 1965 : William Culican, *The Medes and Persians*, Praeger, New York, 1965

Ghirshman, *Parthian and Sassanian Dynasties*, 1962 : Roman Ghirshman, *Persian Art 249 B.C. - A.D. 651 The Parthian and Sassanian Dynasties*, The Arts of Mankind Series, Golden Press, New York, 1962

Ghirshman, *Ancient Iran*, 1964 : Roman Ghirshman, *The Art of Ancient Iran*, The Arts of Mankind Series, Golden Press, New York, 1964

Glueck, *American Journal of Archaeology*, XLI, 1937: Nelson Glueck, "A Newly Discovered Temple of Atargatis and Hadad at Khirbet et-Tannur, Transjordan," *American Journal of Archaeology*, XLI, 1937

Glueck, *Bulletin of the Cincinnati Art Museum*, 1941: Nelson Glueck, "The Nabataean Temple of Khirbet Tannur, Transjordan," *Bulletin of the Cincinnati Art Museum*, XII, 1, Jan. 1941

Glueck, *Deities*, 1965 : Nelson Glueck, *Deities and Dolphins*, Farrar Straus and Giroux, New York, 1965

Glueck, *Jordan*, 1940 : Nelson Glueck, *The Other Side of the Jordan*, American Schools of Oriental Research, New Haven, 1940

Glueck, *Rivers*, 1959 : Nelson Glueck, *Rivers in the Desert*, Farrar Straus and Cudahy, New York, 1959

Goldman, *Art Quarterly*, XXVII, 3, 1964 : Bernard Goldman, "Early Iranian Art in the Cincinnati Art Museum," *The Art Quarterly*, XXVII, 3, 1964

Grabar, *Sasanian Silver*, 1967 : Oleg Grabar, "An Introduction to the Art of Sasanian Silver," exhibition catalog *Sasanian Silver*, University of Michigan, 1967

In Honor of the Shah, New York, 1949-50 : *Exhibition in Honor of the Shah*, Asia Institute, New York, 1949-50

Kantor, *Cincinnati Art Museum Bulletin*, Oct. 1957 : Helene J. Kantor, "Goldworks and Ornaments from Iran," *Cincinnati Art Museum Bulletin*, V, 2, Oct. 1957

Kantor, *Journal of Near Eastern Studies*, XIX, 1, 1960 :
Helene J. Kantor, "A Fragment of a Gold Applique
from Ziwiye and Some Remarks on the Artistic
Traditions of Armenia During the Early First
Millenium, B.C.," *Journal of Near Eastern Studies*,
University of Chicago Press, XIX, 1, Jan. 1960

Near Eastern Art, Cincinnati, 1962 : *Near Eastern Art/
Ancient and Islamic*, Cincinnati Art Museum, 1962

Persian Art, New York, 1940 : *Exhibition of Persian
Art*, Iranian Institute, New York, 1940

Pope, *Masterpieces*, 1945 : Arthur Upham Pope,
Masterpieces of Persian Art, Dryden Press, New
York, 1945

Sasanian Silver, Michigan, 1967 : *Exhibition of Sasanian Silver*, Museum of Art, University of Michigan,
Aug. 13-Sept. 30, 1967

Schmidt, *Persepolis*, 1, 1953 : Erich F. Schmidt,
Persepolis, The University of Chicago Press (Oriental Institute Publications Vol. LXVIII), 1953, Vol. I

Sculpture of Greater India, C. T. Loo, 1942, : *Exhibition of Sculpture of Greater India*, C. T. Loo, Inc.,
New York, 1942; catalog text by John Pope, Bradford Press, New York

Shine, *Museum News*, Feb. 1964 : C. R. Shine, "The
Registrar/Curator without Portfolio," *Museum
News*, Feb. 1964

Survey of Persian Art, 1939, 1966 : *A Survey of Persian
Art*, Arthur Upham Pope and Phyllis Ackerman
editors, Oxford University Press, Asia Institute, London, New York, 1938-39, Tokyo, 1966

7000 ans d'art en Iran, Paris, 1961 : *7000 ans d'art en
Iran*, Petit Palais, Paris, Oct. 1961-Jan. 1962

Index of Artists

The design and typography of this book are by Noel Martin,
assisted by Dana Martin. It is composed in
Georg Trump's Mediaeval type by the C. E. Weber Type Foundry of
Stuttgart, Germany. It was set by Craftsman Type, Dayton, Ohio.
The offset lithography is by Young & Klein, Inc. and
the bookbinding is by Cincinnati Bindery, both of Cincinnati.